The Essential Guide for

Anatomy and Physiology

Yvonne Wood and
Erika Ayling

thewriteidea

Published by The Write Idea Ltd
8 Station Court
Station Road
Great Shelford
Cambridge
CB22 5NE
01223 847765

First published April 2008
ISBN 978-0-9559011-0-2

Set in 10.5/15 Minion Pro.

Printed by Scotprint, Haddington.

CONTENTS

Section 1 – Preparing to Study

Section 2 – Study Techniques

Section 3 – Revision Planning

Section 4 – Exam Preparation

Section 5 – Worksheets and reference materials

ABOUT THE AUTHORS

Yvonne Wood

Yvonne Wood qualified as a complementary therapist 18 years ago and has continued to train in all aspects of complementary therapy.

She has taught for 15 years in both private and local authority education, establishing a wide range of complementary courses as curriculum manager. Being passionate about the quality of teaching in colleges, she also established a successful mentoring scheme for new tutors, with many qualifying to teach diploma courses.

Yvonne has also been involved in fund raising for special schools and other good causes, been guest speaker for various establishments including the Ladies Rotary Lunch and is founding member and chairperson of the Hillingdon Therapists Club. She is currently joint director of Heatherwood Academy.

Erika Ayling

After many years working in Histopathology for the NHS Erika embarked on a career change into complementary therapy. For the last ten years she has trained and practised in many aspects of complementary therapy which ultimately led into teaching.

Erika is particularly inspired by appropriate aftercare for sports activity and has worked with local sporting clubs and youth sports teams. She has taught in both private and local authority establishments, with a guiding ethos of passion, knowledge and nurture. She is currently joint director of Heatherwood Academy.

Heatherwood Academy is a private training provider for complementary and beauty courses. It is ITEC registered and has accreditation with CThA, APNT, and BABTAC. It offers a variety of courses from foundation ITEC units to post graduate CPD courses and workshops. The ethos shared by Yvonne and Erika for the Academy is:

'to provide high quality tutoring in a supportive environment'

www.heatherwoodacademy.co.uk

FROM THE PUBLISHER

Thank you for purchasing this book. We hope that you will find it useful and informative as you progress through your studies. This is the first in what we hope will be a successful series of resource guides.

The overwhelming response we have received from piloting the materials is that these guides will be a valuable asset to any student of complementary or beauty therapy.

One of the main considerations when planning the guides has been to give the content as broad an appeal as possible. Consequently they are written and designed to be useful for anyone studying for a qualification offered by any of the major awarding bodies.

We would welcome any constructive feedback that you can give us. It is only by hearing which parts of the book are useful, or not, that we will be able to improve it for the next edition. Also, if you have any useful hints and tips that you have found particularly effective when teaching or studying we would like to hear about them. We will include the best examples in the next edition.

If you would like to give us your views on this guide please call Andy Wilson on 01223 846445 or email andy@writeidea.co.uk.

ACKNOWLEDGEMENTS

We would like to thank the following for their invaluable assistance in reviewing the draft manuscript of this book:

Jan Jones, Senior Education and Development Manager, CIBTAC

Debbie Nolan, Level 3 Course leader, Amersham and Wycombe College

INTRODUCTION

Whether you are returning to study after years away from the classroom, or advancing into further education, this guide will suggest techniques that will assist you on your journey through the course.

Few people are fortunate enough to have discovered one particular method of learning which is effective in all aspects of their particular style. This guide has been designed to encompass all learning styles and variations of study methods.

Memory is the key issue with any kind of course, recalling the relevant information at the right time. There are ways to improve the capabilities of your memory that will develop an interest in the subject and expand the capabilities of the brain's organisation and volume. Techniques will be discussed to assist your memory and improve on classroom and independent study.

Preparation for study is an important topic that is explained in detail, helping you to ensure that all aspects of your course are fully covered, and that you can achieve maximum benefit from each session. The advantages of both group and self study are discussed.

Revision timetables and exam techniques are explained, to try to minimise the anxiety and stress which are often associated with exam time. This guide can be used alongside your course book, offering ongoing advice on all aspects of study and revision techniques.

It has not been written specifically for any one syllabus or awarding body as the authors and publisher feel that good study skills and revision techniques are generic and are universally applicable, regardless of syllabus or assessment method.

KEY TO ANATOMICAL LANGUAGE

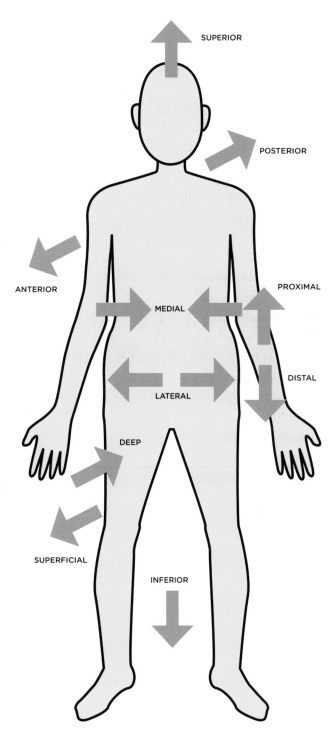

Superior	Towards the head
Inferior	Towards the feet
Anterior/ ventral	Front/belly
Posterior/ dorsal	Back
Medial	Middle
Lateral	Side, away from midline
Proximal	Close, nearest to the point of attachment (referring to arms and legs)
Distal	Distant, farthest from the point of attachment (referring to arms and legs)
Superficial	Towards the surface
Deep	Away from the surface, internal
Supine	Laying face up
Prone	Laying face down
Axial	Head, neck and trunk, skull, vertebral column, rib cage
Appendicular	Portion of skeleton comprising the upper and lower limbs and their girdles

SECTION 1
PREPARING TO STUDY

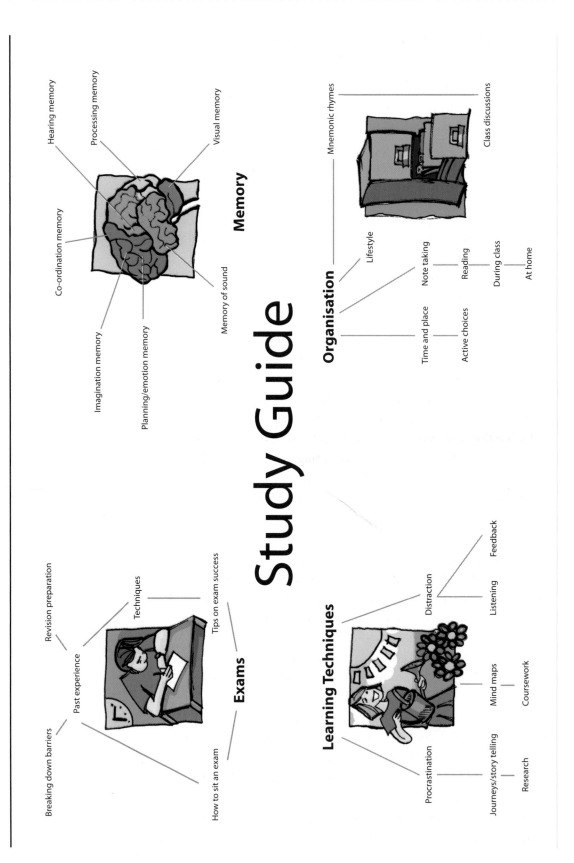

Study Guide

Memory

- Hearing memory
- Processing memory
- Visual memory
- Co-ordination memory
- Memory of sound
- Imagination memory
- Planning/emotion memory

Organisation

- Mnemonic rhymes
- Class discussions
- Lifestyle
- Note taking
- Reading
- During class
- At home
- Time and place
- Active choices

Exams

- Revision preparation
- Techniques
- Tips on exam success
- Past experience
- Breaking down barriers
- How to sit an exam

Learning Techniques

- Distraction
- Feedback
- Listening
- Mind maps
- Coursework
- Procrastination
- Journeys/story telling
- Research

1.1 How the brain stores memories

'Memory is the library of the mind' – Francis Fauvel-Gourand

Some teachers introduce the idea of metacognition to their students by saying, 'You are the owners and operators of your own brain, but it came without an instruction book. We need to learn how we learn.' National Research Council. *How Students Learn.*

These statements reflect on how little we really know about what is required to optimise the workings of our brain and extend its capacity and capabilities. To ensure the learning process is embedded, reflective practise is essential in establishing how learning has taken place and what information has been learnt. This recognition of processes, which enables us to remember facts, telephone numbers, skills, etc is known as *metacognition*.

As shown in the diagram opposite, the brain has many compartments that store specific subject memories. Depending on how the individual's 'filing' system works and how the topic has been related will have an effect on the retrieval process. Managing the millions of messages entering the brain is the process manager, providing a link between all parts of the brain. When establishing information in the correct memory area, each time this action is repeated the connections between the areas become stronger, embedding the knowledge and setting the memory in place.

The brain has a amazing capacity to learn, an ability to change in response to experiences and to retain an expanding library of knowledge throughout a lifetime. This ability to learn and to form new memories is fundamental to our very existence – we rely on memory to engage in effective actions, to understand the written word, to recognise objects, decipher sounds and to establish a personal identity and history. Memory is vital to our everyday existence in providing information regarding safety, daily routine and tasks and at times it is taken for granted – only really being considered when it fails.

There are two main categories of memory, Declarative and Procedural.
DECLARATIVE – this is where factual details are stored and retrieved, e.g. formulae in maths, dates for historical facts, birthdays and anniversaries. Imagine a filing cabinet inside the brain – depending on how the facts are filed and labelled this will indicate how well the memory functions when information recall is requested.
PROCEDURAL – this area focuses on general day-to-day skills and tasks as well as more specific tasks.

The brain has another specific filing area for storing these details, labelled in whatever way the 'processing area' of the brain has decided. This again dictates how effectively the retrieval process takes place.

As a result of the processing of these details, the way to ensure the information is stored in the correct place is *repetition*. For any sort of information to be retained, by constantly repeating the action, or details, the information is repeatedly processed and the connections in the brain between the individual compartments become stronger, with the result that the specific topic, event or task becomes a strong, established memory.

The declarative category of memory is the area that will be used when studying anatomy and physiology – facts and numbers will be processed and stored. Depending on which procedures have been used to study, the repetitive nature of these processes will embed the contents and have an effect on the outcome. Simply learning facts by heart will not have the same long-term effect as understanding the subject and reading articles and books on it.

1.2 Improving your memory

Tips and Techniques for Memory Enhancement

If our brains were like computers, we'd simply install a new microchip to boost or upgrade our memory. However the brain is more complex than even the most advanced piece of technology available today.

Like the muscular system, our memory improves with exercise, as well as a healthy diet and adequate rest.

Memory is divided into two categories based on its duration – it can be either short term or long term. In short term memory, the mind stores information for only a few seconds or minutes – the time it takes for you to remember a number plate or dial a phone number you have just looked up. This memory is delicate and most brains only have the capacity to remember seven figures at a time. That is why you are able to recall the telephone number for the Chinese takeaway but have to have your credit card in front of you when you are paying because you can't remember the sixteen digit number.

Long term memory is the category we are most familiar with, where the information you retain either consciously or subconsciously is stored. Long term memory is used to store information such as birthdays and anniversaries. It is also needed to recall information, for example if you are studying for a test, and to recall events which have had an emotional impact, such as the day your child was born or the day your pet died.

Foundation and Maintenance stages of memory

The brain goes through three processes to enable it to establish form and retain memories.

Acquisition → Consolidation → Retrieval

Acquisition

As new information enters the brain it is transported along pathways between neurons to designated areas. Concentration is the key to locking information into the memory, otherwise it will 'go in one ear and out the other'. This is why teachers should pay particular attention to recapping the information taught within the day's lesson, in order to establish and reinforce the data for the student to recall later.

Consolidation

The brain transmits a signal to store the information as long term memory. This process becomes easier if the data can be related to either an emotional or a physical recollection.

Retrieval

Retrieval of information is easier than storage as the brain will use the same pattern of nerve cells it used to store it. The more frequently this occurs the easier the process will become.

Helping your memory

Students are individuals and everyone learns in different ways. This means that you need to find a way of learning that suits you. This also applies to how you use your memory. There are many ways in which we can improve and enhance our memory in order to train our brain to assist our revision.

1. Work towards a goal

Motivation is the key to success in your studies and you need to feel motivated to study and learn. Identification of your goals is essential and breaking them down into small achievable sections is paramount. You could relate this to losing weight – if you begin a weight management class with the idea you will lose two stone in two weeks you are unlikely to persevere with the programme, because the goal is unrealistic. However, if you aim for a realistic, gradual weight loss of say two pounds a week, when you achieve this you will be motivated to carry on and achieve your long term goal.

2. Relate to a subject

Why is it that sometimes we find some subjects or areas more appealing than others? The answer is the interest factor – if you are interested in what you are doing then concentration naturally follows. Think how easy it is to watch a three hour film or sporting event when it holds your attention. Finding a way to relate to the area of study will promote an interest in it and make the process more enjoyable.

3. The need for breaks

Twenty minutes is the average time for which we can concentrate fully at any one time. After this our concentration will wane, so the first twenty minute period of study or a lesson is the most effective.

4. Read around your subject

This has a number of advantages. It improves your knowledge of the subject and provides different perspectives on it, broadening your interest and deepening your understanding of it.

5. Using your senses

The more senses that are involved in studying, the more you will learn. If you are a visual learner, reading out loud, singing or reciting in a rhythmic way is also beneficial. Relating information to colours, tastes and smells can also help to embed information in our memory.

6. Rehearse information frequently

Recall what you have learned later on after your class. This will embed the knowledge gained, enabling the brain to transfer the information from its short term to long term memory.

7. Music

Some people find that listening to music can help them work more effectively, this is due to the complex structure of the brain. The left side of the brain is used more when studying whilst the right side of the brain is involved with listening to the music, thus preventing daydreaming when trying to concentrate.

8. Memory aids

Memory aids are useful to help you remember pieces of information. Here are some examples which may help you to learn more easily:

- **Mind maps** are an excellent learning tool, the brain's thinking process begins from a central idea, stimulating other related information and assisting you to organise this in a logical manner. This technique works by mirroring the brain's learning pattern.

- **Organising information** If we think of our brains as a filing system, by organising the stored information it is easier to recall it.
- **Mnemonics** This technique involves the association of the information we want to remember with a visual image, a sentence or a word. Common types of mnemonic include:
  - *Visual images* – e.g. a saxophone to remember the name 'Stanley', or a carnation for 'Carol'. Try to use positive, pleasant images, as the brain wills often block out unpleasant associations.
  - *Sentences* – e.g. to remember the solar system a sentence is composed using the initial letter of each planet. For example:
    My Van Engine Makes Joyful Sounds Unlike Noisy People =
    Mercury
    Venus
    Earth
    Mars
    Jupiter
    Saturn
    Uranus
    Neptune
    Pluto
  - *Jokes* – transferring facts, figure and names we need to recall into funny situations are easier to recall than mundane images.
  - *Rhymes and alliteration* – Do you remember learning '30 days hath September, April, June and November'? Or how do we remember to change the clocks twice a year – 'Spring forward and Fall back'. By using these rhymes our brains find it easier to retrieve stored information.

1.3 Preparation for study

Studying is a very personal matter and what will work for one student may not be successful for another. It is important to develop the most effective methods for each individual. Identifying which type of learner you are is the key and this will be discussed in greater detail later on.

Unfortunately, if you are looking for instant success then you are probably heading for failure. Good organisation and thorough working practices are the best recipe for success.

Why do we study?

- For each course that you embark on you must ask yourself 'Why do I want to know', 'What do I want to know' and 'Will the course meet my expectations?'
- Make certain that you are aware of the level of study and commitment required.

Where do we study?

- Having somewhere to study is important. Try to make it the same place each time – this does not have to be a conventional desk. If you are happier sitting on the floor or on the bed then do so. Organise the area so you have all your equipment to hand. Make sure there is adequate lighting and good ventilation, as working in a stuffy environment induces tiredness.
- Beware of distractions! By avoiding these as much as possible, such as turning off the phone, studying during school hours, banishing partners and pets, you will achieve a more effective study time.

Planning your study

- Identify your areas of strength and weakness for each subject and adjust the timing of your revision to fit in with your findings.

- Decide to tackle your most challenging subjects when you are fresh and alert and discipline yourself to deal with them and not put them off in favour of an easier topic.
- Use a diary or calendar to help you to organise your routine. Checking this regularly will help to avoid deadlines creeping up unexpectedly.
- Work out a timetable and STICK TO IT.
- Focus on the task in hand and you may well find that the assignment does not take as long as you were expecting.
- Allow for warming up when you begin a study period and do not expect to achieve maximum output as soon as you sit down.
- It is important to remember that some of the most valuable study can be achieved through discussion with fellow students.
- Work out your best time for study, whether this is first thing in the morning or last thing at night.
- Leave time for yourself. To maintain a positive mood consider taking a break for a while to do something you enjoy.

Equipment

- Post-it notes are invaluable. If possible have access to the Internet, a dictionary or thesaurus, pens, scribbling pads and any reference books that you may need.
- Check the syllabus. You need to make sure that what you're revising is actually on the syllabus and therefore may appear in the exam. Use the syllabus as a check list, and tick things off when you've done them.

Note-taking tips

Why take notes in class?

- Organised notes will help you identify and focus on the most important ideas presented in class.
- A permanent written record will aid your learning and help you to recall information later, keeping you on top of both the theory and the coursework.

- The tutor may provide information in the lesson which is not available anywhere else. This may be your only chance to record it.
- Keep your notes up to date and stored in an organised way, perhaps using a folder or labels to identify different subjects.
- Be brief in your note taking. Summarise your notes in your own words, not the tutor's. Remember that you are trying to understand what they are saying, not recording everything word for word.

Classroom involvement

- It might sound obvious but if you don't understand something then ask questions. It doesn't make you look weak if you don't know the answer. Ask your tutor or your friends in class for help and you may even find that they are stuck on the same problem.
- Try to participate fully in the classroom activities, it is easier to consolidate your learning when you are interested and having fun.

Handling homework

Procrastination

We are all guilty of this at some time in our lives. However, excessive procrastination can result in feeling guilty about not doing a task or homework when it should be done. It can also cause anxiety until it is done. Furthermore, procrastination can lead to poor results if you do not leave sufficient time to do the task well. In short, don't put off until tomorrow what you can do today.

It is essential to keep on top of your homework. Ideally you should complete your homework tasks as soon as you can after the lesson whilst it is still fresh in your mind. If the homework involves research, make sure you allow sufficient time to complete this.

Organisation

In what order do I complete the assignment? If you are having difficulty deciding try seeing the 'whole picture' of the tutor's presentation then break it down into manageable segments. By doing this the task will seem more achievable. Sometimes getting starting is the hardest part!

1.4 Physical requirements for successful study

Quality Sleep

Our brain requires a minimum of seven to eight hours of quality sleep each night to enable the storage of information from that day. If this period is reduced, or the sleep is broken, the process may be interrupted and may result in either incomplete or incorrect storage.

When we are in a deep sleep this is known as 'REM' or Rapid Eye Movement. This was discovered in 1953 byAserinsky and Kleitman. Through the use of a device that monitors brain activity, an *electroencephalogram (EEG)*, these recordings show the 'workings' of the neurons inside the brain passing received information to be processed. They found that the EEG readings of the brain during REM sleep were almost identical to those recordings taken whilst the subjects were awake. These results demonstrate that the brain is very active during REM, storing and processing information from the day's activities into the appropriate memory files. The graphs of an EEG depict the levels of neuron energy in the form of spikes, indicating the level of activity and response to the information. This is why if you are woken from an REM sleep state your memory of the dream is extremely vivid. This is due to sensory information not having been processed. At this time images are formed from memory, which could have multiple meanings. On waking, the rational part of our brain deciphers the correct image in order to maintain the correct functioning of the body.

If the body is deprived of adequate quality sleep there are a number of adverse effects that may occur, such as increased weight, slowed reactions, poor concentration and memory loss. There are also physiological reasons for needing sufficient sleep. Your body needs to shut down its systems, or maintain a low level of input to allow for repairs and essential maintenance to be completed. The value of catnapping should not be underestimated. A short 10 or 15 minute nap can refresh both mind and body, allowing you to finish off your study session successfully.

Sleep is essential for effective mental and physical performance – essential requirements for successful study. When you are studying a complex subject like anatomy and physiology you need to be able to store and retrieve information quickly and efficiently in order to be successful.

Balanced diet and water intake

Why does the body require water and how much is adequate?

The brain represents ⅕₀th of our entire body weight and requires ⅟₂₀th of the blood supply. Water is responsible for more than two thirds of our body weight – the brain is 95% water, the circulation 82% and the lungs 90%. Water is an essential requirement for the nervous system to work effectively, enabling neurons to pass information to each other through the system.

When there is a depletion of water of just 2% dehydration begins, with a negative effect on our short term memory and our ability to focus on print and computer screens. Energy levels in the brain are decreased and headaches or migraines can occur. Stress levels also increase, causing further dehydration, and an increasing cycle of dehydration could develop.

The need for constant fluid intake, preferably water, will assist not only the brain's activity but also the physiological workings of all body systems. The body requires oxygen to breathe, food for fuel and water to maintain all the internal functions. It serves as a lubricant, the base for saliva, forms fluids surrounding joints, controls metabolism, assists in the regulation of body temperature and aids the elimination of waste.

When studying, you should ensure that you have a supply of water to drink at regular intervals, reducing the risk of dehydration and its negative effects on the study session. Vast amounts of information are processed by the brain which require specific storing in order that the 'retrieval' procedure is successful.

The cognitive workings must be fast, efficient and developmental, maintaining a constant flow of information for processing. Keep the brain and body awake and alert, bathed in water internally.

Why does a balanced diet assist studying?

For the brain to work at optimum levels it needs a balance of various elements within the diet – unsaturated fats, complex carbohydrates, sugars, trace elements, vegetables and proteins. The most effective learning will take place when you maintain a balanced diet. High sugar intake can affect concentration levels so suitable snacks whilst studying should include fruits, nuts and seeds. These will aid concentration without affecting sugar levels in the body and reducing brain activity.

Breakfast is the most important meal of the day. As the word indicates, it 'breaks fast', the last meal was the previous evening and the body has fasted throughout the night. The first meal breaks the fast, giving the body fuel for the day's activities. Many studies have shown that not eating a proper breakfast causes reduced performance throughout the day. This is due to the brain's need for a steady supply of glucose.

Beans on toast is the ideal breakfast. Beans provide a good source of fibre, and research has shown an improvement in cognition with a high fibre diet. In addition there is glucose in the toast.

Eggs are rich in choline, which is essential for the production of acetylcholine, a neurotransmitter. By increasing the amount of this neurotransmitter the ability to remember is increased and age related memory loss will be slowed down. Oily fish contains essential omega 3 fatty acids and should been eaten at least once a week. The fatty acids feed the brain and protect against dementia. Lean meat, beans and pulses increase iron levels, assisting in carrying oxygen to the brain.

Salads and fresh fruit contain antioxidants – beta carotene, as well as vitamins C and E, assisting in 'mopping up' free radicals, keeping the brain in optimum condition and slowing down the ageing process. Bananas are high in potassium, providing stamina, and green vegetables increase magnesium levels and reduce stress, all helping to keep your brain healthy and alert.

Yoghurt contains the amino acid tyrosine, required for the production of dopamine and noradrenalin neurotransmitters. Studies have shown that when there is a depletion of this amino acid through stress, memory and alertness are affected.

A diet complete with vegetables, lean meat, fruit, fish, nuts, dairy products and beans will ensure that the brain and body are supplied with the essential nutrients to help promote effective study.

Alcohol consumption should be kept to a minimum during studying as the chemicals in the alcohol interfere with the pathways of the neurons delivering messages. This also applies to any prescription drugs that may have to be taken throughout the course.

The importance of relaxation when studying

Exercise

Thirty minutes of moderate exercise daily will ensure the brain receives a good supply of oxygen to support all its essential functions. In addition, the body's systems will benefit from improved circulation, increasing oxygen and nutrient levels and the removal of wastes and toxins.

Endorphins are released during physical activity, giving a feeling of well-being, decreasing stress levels and helping to promote quality study.

Complementary treatments

There are numerous benefits which can be derived from any complementary treatment. They are stress busting, calming and at the same time emotionally uplifting. Complementary treatments help to achieve homeostasis of mind, body and emotions and positive results can be achieved on receiving just a single treatment.

Time out from study is an important element of the whole programme, ensuring that you adopt a balanced approach to your studies. The old saying that 'all work and no play makes Jack a dull boy', may sound simplistic but its message holds true for anyone embarking on an intensive course of study.

Meditation

To clear the mind of the day's stresses is like tidying your house. Making room for the next session enables the learning process to be completed more effectively.

Meditation calms and clears the mind, allowing thought processes to be halted and giving time out for the brain to 'catch up'. The effect on the brain is to switch off, giving a power nap, refreshing and stimulating providing renewed energy to carry on, or alternatively to prepare you for sleep.

In the early 1920s Edmund Jacobson developed the 'Jacobson's Progressive Muscle Relaxation' technique. He argued that anxiety accompanies muscular tension, so by reducing the tension in the muscles through relaxation stress can also be reduced. For anatomy and physiology students knowledge of this technique is essential in understanding how the muscular system works and how it directly relates to effective relaxation and improved study sessions.

There are many activities that are classified as leisure or relaxation. These may include listening to music, gardening, painting, sports, needlework, etc. The secret is to establish what works for you and to include that activity as part of your study timetable.

Word puzzle

To remind you of all the necessary 'ingredients' for successful study find
the following words in the word puzzle below.

memory	revision	timetables	sleep
water	diet	homework	time
equipment	techniques	procrastination	reviewing
visual	physical	organisation	preparation
declarative	procedural	repetition	

```
l t t i e l s e o e e i r e a o e d p o v b c l s
t o r e r i w l k i h i r u t n r p u i t r m s p
r t s s i i r n e n l i i n r e p t s r n n c r i
s n a m i n o a o e t a o c s s c m u n i i e o m
r r i t h i r i w a p i c e n e m h t i t a a s v
l t p t s s t t a r t w r i t n h r n t i r t o p
e i e i o i t t b a a t l p s d m a d i h e r i e
r l v q t w q r s t e s i e s y o t y u q e p u w
e e i e a p e i t n t y a w h l e u v u l t l
r e p l n q n r a e o s s p r r p p e i i r e p r
i e g p u a p a n i e t r m e o i i e p e y t s p
r q t s g r o i t o s l i l i e m w n r r i e e c
r t a r t a v a c e i t h r w r i e w a m m n p t
r i o v p l r p c n u t s p c n e d m e m a l e i
c u n e l a p i o s e o a r g t r e a y d a a e u
n a i i p t e p r a s e i n t r i e h o r e v e o
r p g e h p v m y e t h m b i n e e i u y i d n y
v r r r t o a n l v s n r r m t r n d m t r e i n
o p i t s m m b q u i t e i c b s e s a n u i s o
u o n k e d a e r i l s a m h r c a r t k s n r i
o w i e t t u u w n l i u o p o v a r q c d e t s
i i r m e m u n a o e k o a r i l s n c i v t l p
b i n m l g r t t c r c k p l c u o p e o e c m a
p o i p s a n e i p c k r p e a a q t d r r r w e
a t r n o a u n y r r a o d p u s p e e d r p u e
```

SECTION 2
STUDY TECHNIQUES

2.1 Study methods to suit learning styles

Have you ever tried to learn something simple and not been able to grasp the concept? Or tried to teach people and found them confused by what you considered to be a basic fact? If so, then you may have experienced a clash of learning styles. When this happens it can be frustrating for all concerned and it may result in a breakdown in communication and the failure of the teaching/learning process. Everyone has a different learning style and many of us even have a combination of two or more different styles.

You should establish your learning style at the start of the course, enabling your tutor to create a balanced learning environment in which everyone's needs are met. This will enable you to achieve your goals with background support from the tutor available when needed. The three main ways in which people study are:

a) perceiving the information

b) processing the information

c) organising and presenting the information

When gathering information to help us study we use all our senses. Some of us employ one sense more than others. The VARK system assesses how much people rely on sight, hearing, reading, writing and other stimuli. *Kinaesthetic* learners are tactile and respond to movement and activity, meaning they prefer to learn through hands-on activities rather than reading books or listening to lectures. Ann *auditory* learner prefers to listen and absorb information rather than taking part in an activity.

Once the student has acquired information, for example by visual or auditory communication, they will process it in to their own preferred way. Some may prefer to receive facts in a logical, sequential way in order to build a picture one step at a time, while others may prefer to have an overview straight away and process the details later. The final step in the learning process is organising and presenting the information, and again individual preference is the key. Within a classroom environment some students may prefer to present information using visual aids, while others will use a more logical, detailed approach. In order to programme your own study time effectively you will need to decide what suits your own learning style.

What are the main types of learning style?

Visual learners – learning through seeing

These learners like to see and read the tutor's body language and facial expressions to fully understand the content of the lesson. They enjoy a stimulating and orderly environment and will prefer to work with diagrams and charts. Reading may well be a hobby and they will probably be good spellers.

Study tips to help people who are visual learners:

- Drawing pictures, using charts and mind maps to assist comprehension.
- Use planners, organisers or goal setting charts.
- Visualise facts and ideas.
- When revising, read over and recopy notes.

Auditory learners – learning through listening

An auditory learner will interpret verbal information by the tone, pitch and speed of the tutor's voice. They will learn best when listening to a lecture, class discussions or debates and written information may have little meaning until it has been heard. Therefore, when studying, an auditory learner may use a tape recorder to process the information.

Study tips to help an auditory learner:

- When you have to learn facts, try to recite them to yourself or sing them aloud.
- Some students study best with music, while others may prefer silence.
- Discussing the topic with your peer group or friends will help to embed what you have just been studying.

'Doing' learners (kinaesthetic)

Kinaesthetic learners will learn best when moving around, remembering information when they have actually performed the task as opposed to reading about it. They tend to take lots of notes in class but then never return to look at them. Spelling and grammar can cause them difficulty.

Study tips to help a kinaesthetic learner:

- Try to review what you have studied while you are busy.
- Use models to help embed information.
- Take plenty of breaks during study to keep your mind fresh and alert.
- Moving around as you learn or revise can be beneficial.

These are some of the main learning styles. In addition to these there are a number of less common categories such as reflective learners, who take time to analyse the information and prefer to work out problems on their own. There are also intuitive learners, who prefer theoretical information. These students will tend to look for the meaning of what they are studying.

To find out your own preferred learning style, complete the chart below. You are likely to have answers in all three columns but there will probably be more in one column than the others.

Once you have identified your own natural learning preference you can work on expanding the way you learn. By understanding this, and developing the skills that help you learn in a variety of ways, you will make the most of your learning potential. Take time to identify your own learning style and then force yourself to break out of your comfort zone.

When you...	Visual	Auditory	Kinaesthetic
Read	Do you like descriptive scenes or pause to imagine the scenes?	Do you enjoy conversation or hearing the characters talk?	Are you not a keen reader and/or do you prefer action stories?
Spell	Do you try and see the word?	Do you say the word aloud?	Do you write the word down to see if it looks right?
Learn a new computer programme	Do you follow the diagrams in the instruction booklet?	Do you discuss with people who already have the programme?	Do you use the controls or keypad?
Look for new websites	Do you like the interesting design or features?	Like the ones that play music or interviews?	Do you prefer the ones that you can click on or use the shift key?
Complete a test or an exam and accept feedback	Would you prefer to use graphs to show what you have achieved?	Rather have somebody talk through the paper with you?	Do you use examples to show what you have done?
Meet someone again	Do you remember their face but forget their name?	Do you remember names but not faces? Can you also recall information from the last conversation?	Do you remember best the details about the day you spent together?
Concentrate	Do you become distracted by an untidy desk or someone moving around?	Do you become distracted by background noise or someone talking in the same room?	Do you become distracted by activity and would rather join in with what's going on?

2.2 Defining important elements of each body system

Human biology can appear daunting, with many intricate details to remember. The body is the most fascinating machine, working constantly all day, every day. To successfully study any topic you need to be interested and thirsty for knowledge. This will enhance your understanding of the topic and promote a desire to research independently. It is also essential to ensure the methods used suit the individual's learning needs and are not merely adapted from past experiences or from a lack of any other option. Furthermore there is a need to structure the elements of each topic into manageable chunks of information. There is a saying that 'you would never eat a whole elephant, but cut it into small pieces and the task is not so daunting!'

These chunks of information need to be relevant and easily pieced together, like building blocks, enabling a complete picture to be formed and knowledge constructed and built upon.

Each system of the body has its own specialised structure, designed to cope with the functions and processes that are required of it. Having a thorough understanding of the way each system works is an essential foundation on which to build a deeper understanding of how the body works. The systems can develop problems that result either in conditions or diseases. When studying consider what could go wrong and what effect this would have on the organs involved. Make a table for each system in your workbooks and 'build' the contents as each one is revised.

2.3 Structures

The structure of each system is important and requires careful revision to establish a foundation on which to build the other key elements. In this section we examine the structure of each system in turn and provide exercises to test your knowledge. Once the structures are familiar to you we will discuss each system's processes and functions in the next section. This way of revising involves 'chunking' the information into easily-digestible bite-sized pieces. Building knowledge of a system in stages can be much more productive than learning the whole system at once. This starts with understanding how it is built and then moving on to how it works. This section has been designed to offer guided revision, as the basic knowledge should have already been taught on your course. This divides the revision into two parts – the working structures and the functions and processes.

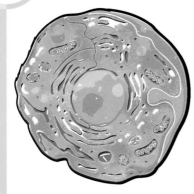

The cell

You should be able to recognise the cell structure and the names of all the organelles before moving on to the processes and functions.

Consider the structure of the outer layer of the cell. What does it need to achieve? There has to be a control on substances entering and leaving the cell, just as a security officer monitors the entrance and exits to a building. The outer layer prevents bacteria from entering the cell structure and also controls the size of molecules passing through it.

The outer covering is known as a semi-permeable membrane, or selective membrane, permitting entry to substances or gases. The delivery methods have to be appropriate to the 'contents' that are being transported – just as we have lorries, ships, trains and aircraft to transport different types of goods. What are the differences in the methods? And are they relevant to the 'goods' being carried? Now consider each transport method and write down all the substances each are responsible for 'carrying', noting the 'special' activity that each method uses to enter the cell's structure.

Label the blank diagram of the cell on page 114 to help reinforce your understanding of the substances they carry and the methods used.

Each part of the cell has an individual function for maintaining the healthy development and workings of the cell. The parts are 'held' in position by a jelly like substance, cytoplasm, which holds the organelles and provides enzymes and other substances in order that functions can be performed. Think of the cell as a factory that has to produce an end product on a production line. Fill in the blanks in the following sentences with the relevant organelle names:

Power or energy: ....

Transport: ....

Packaging: ....

Waste disposal: ....

Storage areas: ....

Supervisor/owner responsible for growth, repairs and development:

....

Specialist workers provide essential materials: ....

Workers responsible for reproducing parts: ....

Security guards: ....

Transport of fluids: ....

Transport of gases: ....

Transport of large items: ....

Transport of fats: ....

Raw materials required: ....

To revise the organelles, transport methods and materials required, complete the blanks and consider their functions within the cell.

1. The cell membrane works as a .... filter.

2. Movement of substances from a high concentration to an area of lower concentration is known as d ....

3. Osmosis is the process of transferring .... across the .... by osmotic pressure until they are ....

4. When fatty substances are too big to diffuse through the membrane and reduction of the molecules takes place, this is known as ....

5. If substances are too large and cannot be reduced, they are 'carried' through the membrane, this is known as .... transport.

6. The .... method of transport is the movement of water soluble substances pushed across the cell membrane caused by the difference in the pressure on either side.

By first understanding the cell's structure, you can then revise how its structure relates to its function. In any organisation there is a supervisor controlling activities and managing processes. In the cell this is called the nucleus. This part of the cell needs protecting and has its own security to prevent unauthorised entry, ensuring that the contents are not harmed and are allowed to function uninterrupted. This is the area that initiates a duplicate cell to be made and contains the genetic 'blueprint' of the body, DNA, enabling the cells to repair and the body to grow.

Once the basic structure of the cell has been revised the next stage is to broaden your understanding and knowledge of it. This will be discussed later in the section on functions and processes.

Tissues

Just as building a house requires special materials for different parts of the structure, so the body needs different types of tissue to perform the different functions that are required of it. In a house insulation is required to conserve heat and prevent pipes from bursting, similarly the body has to maintain its temperature and protect its internal workings. If the correct body temperature is not maintained then homeostasis is lost, causing adverse effects on our health and possibly even death if the situation remains unchecked for too long.

Tissue type	Functions	Locations in body
Epithelial simple 1. Squamous 2. 3. 4.	Provides smooth linings.	Heart lining, blood vessels, alveoli.
Epithelial compound 1. 2.		
Connective 1. 2. 3. 4. 5. 6. 7. 8.		
Muscular		
Nervous		

When revising the tissues think of them as materials required for building a body. Use the blank body on page 115 to fill in where each type of tissue is required and why. Each area of the body needs a particular type of tissue in order to perform correctly and each tissue type is specifically designed to meet the needs and requirements of its part of the body. For example, if the mouth did not have tissue that provided lubrication, what effect would that have on the functions of the mouth? There are some areas that require dryness, others need lubrication. Using the table on the previous page and the body diagram on page 115 for reference, name the tissue types and consider the functions required for that area of the body.

Skeletal system

The skeleton is made of bone, a type of tissue, and forms the framework of the body. Without it the body would have no shape or form onto which our organs could be attached.

The skeletal structure is shaped to accommodate the many different organs and functions required by our body. It is very important to know the shape and names of the main bones and to establish their position in the skeleton. It is also important to know the difference between the axial skeleton, the body's main frame, and the appendicular skeleton, which comprises the attachments or limbs, attached to the main frame.

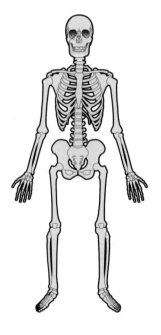

Think about the strength of the skeleton and why certain areas might have a different bone structure to others. How would it feel to collide into another person or object if you didn't have any bones? Imagine walking without a skeleton. Could this be achieved? The skeletal system moves through muscle attachment. Joints are formed to permit flexibility and a whole range of intricate movements. There are 206 named bones in the body, so the most effective way to learn them is to divide them into different areas and work through each section in turn.

Vertebra areas and number of bones	
Area	No. of bones

Names of the bones in the skull

F ....

P ....

V ....

Man ....

M ....

T ....

L ....

P ....

S ....

O ....

Z ....

T ....

H ....

E ....

N ....

The shoulder girdle consists of two ………….. and two ………………… .

The pelvic girdle consists of three …………………………… bones

These are ……………… , ……………… , …………………… .

The arm has the …………………… bone in the upper arm, the lower part

consists of the …………. and ………………… .

Each wrist has ……carpels, the hand has …… metarcarpels, each finger

has ……….. p …………… bones and each thumb has ………. .

The ankle has seven …………… bones and …………. metatarsals. Each

toe has …………. p…………bones and ……… in each big toe.

To memorise these divide the skeleton into parts and work on each area individually. Firstly think about the structure of the skull and name all the bones before moving on to the next part. Divide the skeleton into skull, trunk, pelvic girdle, arms, legs and feet. Work through each area in turn until you are happy that you know all the relevant bones in the skeleton.

By first understanding the structure of the skeleton it will be easier to move on to the functions and processes which follow.

Muscular system

There are three types of muscle tissue – *voluntary*, *involuntary* and *cardiac*. Muscles help the body to move as a result of their attachment to our bones. There are over 640 named muscles in the body, some superficial, near the surface, and others deep within the body tissue. Muscles help to provide a range of movements for each specific area of the body, enabling us to perform a variety of complex activities.

All muscles are attached to bones, supported by cartilage and ligaments at the joint areas. The structure of the different muscles determines how the body moves and performs its daily functions such as balance, posture, movement, digestion, breathing and temperature control. In order to understand the muscular system, we need to know where the different kinds of muscular tissue are found.

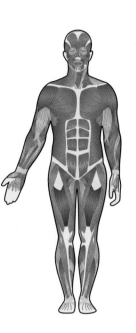

Voluntary: muscles that cause movement involving the skeletal system.
Examples are ....

Involuntary: automated muscular activity involving the following systems .

....

Cardiac: refers to the the heart muscle. It is specialised and controlled by the *medulla oblongata*, maintaining contractions of the heart 24 hours a day.

Each muscle provides a specific action and also supports the movement of its opposite muscle's action – a prime mover, or .... ,

a supporting muscle or ....

By working in pairs the movement is strong and precise, providing a smooth action.

The two types of contraction are: …………………………….. and

……………………………. .

The contraction that produces movement is called……………………… .

The contraction that requires little movement but increases tension is

called……………………… .

Where a muscle joins to a bone is known as an ………………………………… .

The thickest part of a muscle is called the ………………………………… .

The end of the muscle that moves is known as the ……………………………… .

The end of the muscle that remains still, or hardly moves, is called the

………………………………………………………………………… .

The ability of a muscle to contract can be affected by:

a reduced supply of required gas ……………………………………………… .

adequate blood supply to transport …………………………, ………………………,

……………………………, …………………………… and ……………………… .

build-up of wastes, such as …………………………………………………… .

a reduction in ……………… nerve supply.

a …………………………….in temperature.

The length of time the muscle has been contracting will cause

……………………………. of the muscle.

Study the clues below and think about why muscles can become
overworked.

When these factors occur the result is known as

....

Muscles attach to a bone by a ....

....

Bones attach to bones by a ....

....

Muscles have a protective covering called ....

....

This is a tough, inflexible membrane providing assistance to a muscle
action increasing pressure and tension.

Use the table below to revise the muscles and separate areas of the body.
Make sure you understand each section before moving on to the next one.
Look at the table on the following page. Think about the movements and
fill in a muscle for each section of the body.

Movement	Muscle
Flexion: to flex or bend	
Extension: extension of limb away from body	
Rotation: neck or head rotates	
Abduction: to take away from body	
Adduction: to bring towards the midline	
Pronation: limb to turn face down	
Eversion: foot turns away from body	
Inversion: foot turns towards the body	
Supination: limb turns upward	
Dorsiflexion: toes bend up toward body	
Plantarflexion: toes are 'planted' on the ground	

Trunk Muscles		
Muscle	**Main Movements**	**Location on Body**
Sternocleidomastoid	Flexes neck laterally Rotates	Neck and attaches to sternum and clavicle

'Chunking' this exercise will improve the results. It would be daunting to try and remember all the relevant muscles at once, so revise the muscles in sections – the head, arms, trunk and legs – making sure that you know each group before moving on to the next. You may find it helpful to use the blank diagrams for muscles on pages 116–117 and some colouring pencils.

Circulation, heart and lymph

Blood is a fluid connective tissue, consisting of three main types of cell that each have separate functions. The structure of blood holds clues as to the state of our health, indicating how effectively the body is maintaining supplies of the materials used by our cells. If supplies are low this could indicate an imbalance that may have an effect on how well our body is working.

Red blood cells, *erythrocytes*, are responsible for carrying oxygen to cells and require iron to successfully complete this task. If the number of the red cells is low the amount of oxygen being delivered will be reduced, having an adverse effect on the body.

White blood cells, *leucocytes*, defend the body against bacteria, viruses and toxins. When the white cell count is low, this indicates the body is fighting an infection and will need time to reproduce enough cells to regain the levels of a healthy body.

Thrombocytes form part of the body's clotting mechanism, preventing us from bleeding to death when we are cut. If the numbers are low there is a higher chance of excessive bleeding as the clotting process will take longer.

Plasma is the straw coloured liquid that carries nutrients, waste, enzymes, hormones, mineral salts and antibodies. A large percentage of plasma is water and plasma proteins such as albumin and globulin.

The different components of the blood are circulated in a closed system network of veins and arteries.

The next structure is the 'mapping' of the arteries and the veins. This is similar to a road network – there are wide roads that become smaller roads and then minor roads, finally narrowing to a single track. This reflects the structure of the circulatory system, the wide road being the aorta leaving the heart, gradually narrowing as it progresses through the body, until at cell level it is an arterial capillary. From here the return journey begins with deoxygenated blood collected from the cells, growing from a venal capillary into the vena cava entering the heart.

There are four specific types of circulation in the body.

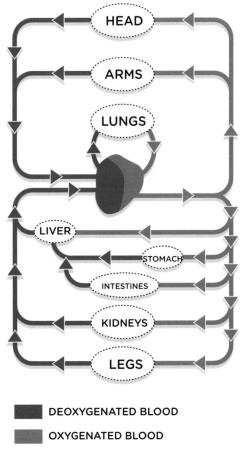

DEOXYGENATED BLOOD

OXYGENATED BLOOD

Systemic circulation: the circulation of blood from the heart to the cells of the body.

Pulmonary circulation: deoxygenated blood from the right ventricle carried in the pulmonary artery to the lungs, then oxygenated blood collected from the lungs into the pulmonary veins and carried back to the left atrium of the heart.

Coronary circulation: the cardiac muscle needs a supply of oxygenated blood to be able to sustain the muscular activity required to pump the blood around the body.

Portal circulation: The veins from the stomach, spleen, pancreas and intestines join together to form the hepatic portal vein, this continues into the liver collecting wastes and moving towards the heart.

The flow of blood has to be controlled in certain areas of the body, in a similar way to how traffic is controlled by traffic lights. Valves exist to control the direction of blood ensuring it is always moving towards the heart.

Study the circulation one section at a time. Look at the blank diagram for arteries and veins on page 119, and use a red pen to trace the route leaving the heart and a blue pen to trace the route of the veins returning to the heart. Remember that the arteries deliver – oxygen, nutrients, hormones, etc and the veins collect – CO_2, waste products, etc. The blood goes one way out from the heart to cellular level and then returns one way back to the heart. This is a useful way of revising direction and structure.

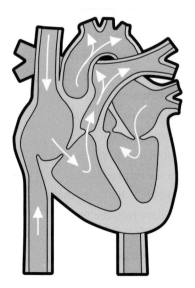

Heart

Knowledge of the heart's structure is essential before being able to move on to the functions and process that are carried out by this tireless pump.

The four chambers in the heart are called the ....

....

The veins that enters the heart carrying deoxygenated blood from the body are the ....

 The veins carrying oxygenated blood from the lungs are the.........................

....

The artery that distributes the blood from the heart to the cellular level is the ....

The valves which prevent a back flow of blood in the right side of the heart are called the ....

The valves which prevent a back flow of blood in the left side of the heart are called the ....

The divider in the heart which prevents blood from different areas mixing is called the ....

Lymph

This system has a structure that is located adjacent to the circulation, in addition to the nodes that are located around the body like cleansing stations. The vessels that carry the lymph fluid are larger than those in the circulatory system and carry both wastes and nutrients. This system is designed to mop up any excess fluid from around the cells and tissues which may contain a mixture of large and small particles. This system is closed, only rejoining the main circulation at specific points on the body, allowing nutrients to be delivered to cells and waste matter to be collected. The position of the nodes needs to be learnt as part of a map showing the flow of lymph and the points where it re-enters the body's circulation.

Lymph fluid – this is the excess fluid surrounding the cells and is known as ……………….. . It contains a mixture of components delivered to cells and the waste products that are excreted. This fluid circulates the lymphatic system and re enters the circulation at the …………………………. .

Lymph nodes – these remove ……………… from the lymph fluid as it passes through the system, acting as ……………………….. stations.

Lymph vessels – these carry lymph around the lymphatic system. They contain valves that ensure the flow of blood is always towards the heart.

Lymph capillaries – these work closely with the circulation collecting the excess fluid from around the tissues, eventually joining together to form lymphatic vessels.

Nervous system

Nervous tissue is highly specialised, having the ability to conduct electricity. It allows neurons to pass information from one part of the body to another to maintain a safe environment and homeostasis. The nervous system is divided into separate parts that each have special functions. Each of their structures needs to be studied individually in order to understand its contribution to the whole system.

Central nervous system – consists of the brain and the spinal column. This is comparable to the electrical wiring in a house, transporting energy from one area to another. The nervous system is controlled by the brain, protected by the spine and supplies the limbs. It is important to understand the 'wiring' and the circuits that are laid down in the body to facilitate a fast communication system which responds to the body's needs.

A neuron is a nerve consisting of several parts, protected by insulating material, similar to the insulation around a wire in an electrical appliance.

As the body's control mechanism and distribution channel, the brain and spine have to be protected. The brain has several compartments, each responsible for specific actions and responses, in addition to areas responsible for memory, hearing, speech, etc.

Think about the different parts of the brain and what they do and form a picture of how they all relate to each other. The structure is the mechanism by which the functions and processes inter-relate. The information arrives in the brain through sensory nerves. They convey messages from our senses relating to hearing, smell, taste, sight and touch, or about changes in our environment. These have to be processed and may involve several different parts of the brain. The brain will then react to these messages and may, for example, order a movement by motor nerves to ensure that we avoid any potential danger.

The brain is capable of processing a vast amount of information and sending out instructions very quickly. However, as the brain grows older its capabilities reduce, or slow down. Memory is not always as accurate as it once was, as the neurons that pass the information in the brain degenerate and become less effective. The same results can occur from a trauma to the central nervous system. If damage has occurred to these structures it can adversely affect their internal workings.

Peripheral nervous system – consists of the sensory and motor nerves. These nerves convey messages from the sensory receptors. These are cells that sense changes in the environment which may affect the function or safety of the body. The motor nerves take the commands from the brain to the areas that need to take action.

Cranial nerves – these are specific to the brain and neck area, dealing with sight, hearing, smell, taste, touch, swallowing, etc.

Spinal nerves – these are divided into groups, or plexuses, that relate to the area of the body in which they are found – cervical, thoracic, lumbar, sacral and coccygeal.

Usually the brain processes all information, except when speed is required to protect the body from harm. This is called a reflex action. Reflex actions occur more quickly than if we wait for the brain to send out a message to command an action. They are produced in response to stimuli, such as a hot plate or sharp object. The sensory nerve carries the information, but only as far as the spinal column, where an automated response will be sent immediately to remove the hand from danger, hence the term 'reflex action'.

Autonomic nervous system (ANS) – consists of an internal automated system, supplying nerves to the organs and circulation vessels. The hypothalamus controls this part of the system and actions are controlled by both reflex and involuntary responses. It is the body's protection and self-preservation system and is divided into two parts.

Sympathetic – enables the body to cope with stressful situations, giving an extra boost of strength when required – the 'fight or flight' mechanism.

Parasympathetic – returns the body to normal by restoring calm and balance, creating a 'rest' period in order that the next stressful time can be successfully managed.

Revise each structure separately and then look at them together to complete your understanding of the nervous system.

Endocrine system

This system works closely with the nervous system and is sometimes called the neuro-endocrine system. It is another communication system working on a slower delivery route, through the circulation rather than at great speed through specialised nervous tissue. The 'messenger' is a hormone that is sent from the system manager – the pituitary gland. In response to the body's needs the hypothalamus passes information to the pituitary which responds by sending a message to the relevant glands to begin producing their own hormone.

The glands are in different areas of the body and depending on which hormones are delivering the messages, they can affect our behaviour and reaction to certain situations.

Think of the endocrine system as an orchestra. The hypothalamus is the manager, telling the pituitary, the conductor, what music is to be played, directing the various musicians in the orchestra when to perform and when to stop playing. All glands need to be constantly told when to perform. The messages have to be continuous until the process is completed.

Complete the blanks on the table on the following page for the endocrine glands. Using the blank body for the endocrine system name all the glands and the hormones they produce. Indicate the pituitary as the master gland with responsibility over the system.

Gland	Location in body	Function
	Brain	
		Controls metabolism
P		Controls calcium levels
		Produces 't' cells
	Pancreas	
A		
Cortex		1. Produces hormones that affect mineral balance in the body 2. Produces hormones that affect glucose balance 3. Produces sex hormones
1. Mineralcorticoids		
2.		
3. Gonadcorticoids		
Medulla		Produces adrenaline
Ovaries		
Testes		

The digestive system

This system deals with the ingestion of solid food, breaking it down into tiny particles for absorption by the cells and the subsequent excretion of waste products. The teeth, tongue, taste buds and salivary glands are located in the mouth and are responsible for the start of the food's journey through the digestive system.

Teeth – chew, grind and tear food into smaller pieces.

Taste buds – distinguish between sweet, sour, salt and bitter.

Tongue – assists in moving food around the mouth and down into the oesophagus.

Salivary glands – moisten food and release salivary amylase, an enzyme that breaks down starches.

Oesophagus – a lubricated tube that transports the food into the stomach. It has a mucus membrane and muscular walls that allow peristalsis, rhythmic contractions of the muscles, to move the food downwards.

Stomach – This is a muscular sac, made of different types of tissue to cope with the many different functions it has to perform. It must be able to expand and contract, be waterproof, able to 'churn' its contents, able to secrete digestive enzymes onto the food and cope with the resulting substances that are produced. Write down what the small intestine consists of:

1. ....

2. ....

3. ....

Inside the intestine the surface is covered with finger-like projections,

'..', that transport the nutrients into the cells.

Large intestine – this removes any remaining water and vitamins before the wastes are formed. The colon can be compared to a plumbing system, with bends that can become blocked. The linings are able to produce mucus and absorb water, and the waste is moved along by peristalsis. Any problems can slow the system down and cause blockages which may prevent the excretion of waste from the body.

Think of this system as a machine, if any part is missing or faulty the functions cannot be completed. Understanding the structures required for a successful digestive system will help you relate the functions and processes to the system.

The respiratory system

The structure of this system requires that oxygen be taken from outside the body into the lungs, then on to the heart to be pumped around the body and distributed to the cells. At the same time the respiratory system removes carbon dioxide from the body via the heart to the lungs and exhales it from the body.

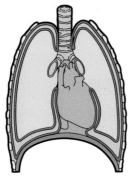

The passage of air

Air is inhaled through the nose or mouth, particles are filtered, it

is.........................and..................................... .

The **pharynx** is where the back of the throat and the nose are joined by a tube. It is part of the ....and ....

systems, dividing into the oesophagus and the larynx.

The **larynx** is the voice box producing the voice by controlling the air over the vocal chords, warms and …………………………………..the air.

The **trachea** has a specialised lining called …………………………. . This type of tissue has a hair-like appearance, which prevents dust particles from entering, and which can be 'swept' up towards the epiglottis and swallowed or taken back to the mouth. The trachea ……………………….. and moistens the air before it enters the lungs.

The **bronchi** are branches from the trachea which lead into the lungs, dividing into the ………………….. . These become smaller and at the end of these are found the …………….., where gaseous exchange takes place.

The lungs sit either side of the heart and are covered by a ……………. which is a serous membrane that protects the surface. They have two layers with a cavity that prevents friction during respiration. To enable the lungs to expand and deflate during respiration, the diaphragm and ………………. muscles are involved in the process.

Using the blank diagram for respiration on page 123, revise the structure, naming the parts and their actions.

The urinary system

The body has two kidneys, each containing millions of 'factories' that have the ability to filter the blood, reabsorb what the body can use and excrete the remainder as urine.

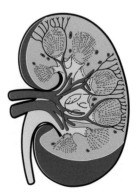

The kidney structure contains the outer part, the ………………………..,

the middle part, the ……………………………..,

and the inner part, the r……………. p…………………………. area.

These factories, or ………………………………, twirl up and down the

kidney, beginning in the c…………………………………….,

the down into the m…………….. returning to the c………………. and

then travelling down to the R………… P ……….. area to deposit the

wastes. Here it enters the …………………., two tubes connected to the

renal pelvic part of the kidney that transport the ………………… to be stored in the ………………….. When the amount reaches 200ml a message is sent to the brain to excrete the waste through the ……………….. .

Using the blank diagram marked nephron, label the following areas: filtration, reabsorption and collection of wastes.

The reproductive system

Female reproductive organs

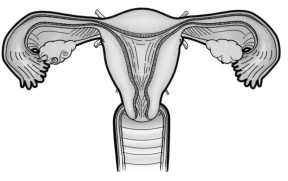

The female reproductive organs consist of:

Ovum – the female sex cell. Eggs are released on a monthly cycle and if one is fertilised by a sperm it is implanted in the uterus forming an ……………. . It then develops into an embryo and after nine months into a baby.

Ovaries – these sit on either side of the uterus, containing ………………. that release eggs, with each side taking turns to release an egg each month.

…………………. tubes – carry the egg from the ovary to the uterus.

Uterus – the womb, where the fertilised ………………. embeds and develops into a baby.

Cervix – ……………. of the uterus that leads to the vagina.

Vagina – A ……………………………. passage that leads from the outside of the body to the cervix of the uterus.

The outer parts of the female reproductive organs comprise the labia minora and labia majora. These protect the entrance to the vagina and the clitoris, a sensitive organ consisting of erectile tissue which fills with blood during sexual activity.

Male reproductive organs

The male reproductive organs consist of the prostate gland. This surrounds the beginning of the urethra and sits between the bladder and rectum.

Testes – two glands situated outside the body, contained within the scrotum.

The ………………….., contained within the testes, is a ………………. that carries the sperm from the testes to the vas deferens.

Vas deferens – A …………………….. that transports the sperm from the epididymis to the urethra.

Penis – Male external sex organ, consists of …………………. tissue, contains a tube for the urethra excreting urine and also acts for semen to be added to the sperm as it leaves the penis.

Glans – this is the tip of the penis, surrounding by the foreskin or prepuce.

Sperm – Male sex cell, containing …………. chromosomes (half the amount for a human body). It has a tail, or ……………………….. , that enable the sperm to swim along the vagina, into the uterus and into the fallopian tubes.

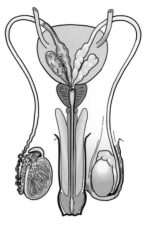

Using the blank diagrams provided for each set of organs on page 125, label the parts and make notes of the functions.

The skin

The skin has two layers. One is responsible for the continuous production of cells, and has five separate layers through which the cells travel maturing as they ascend until they die and are shed. This layer is known as the ………………. . The ……………. or true skin, contains specialised cells called mast cells that produce histamine which protects against allergic reactions and heparin that is part of the clotting mechanism. Cells that fight infection are called ……………….. and those that produce specific tissues to keep the skin supple and flexible are collagen, ………………. and areolar.

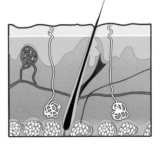

Sensory nerve receptors – receiving signals concerning temperature changes, pressure applied to the skin and pain felt.

Sweat glands – These are situated in the dermis, pass through the epidermis to outside the body. There are two types, …………………….., found all over the body, controlling temperature from birth throughout life. ………………………., situated in the axilla (armpits) and groin areas, develop during puberty and excrete a milky fluid that produces body odour when mixed with bacteria found on the skin's surface.

Sweat contains a large amount of water, urea and salts.

Hair follicles – these sit in the subcutaneous layer and pass through the dermis and epidermis, the ………………………………….. is the tiny projection at the base of each follicle containing blood vessels and nerve supply. The …………………………….. muscles attached to the hairs assist in temperature control.

Sebaceous glands – produce sebum to lubricate hairs and assist in the production of ……………………………………….. which protects the skin.

Blood supply – arterial and venal capillaries to supply and collect from the areas.

Lymphatic capillary – collects excess fluid from the tissues and enters it into the lymphatic system.

With the aid of the skin diagram on page 126 practise labelling the different areas. Consider the two layers, the epidermis and dermis and briefly consider what happens in each layer and why.

2.4 Functions and processes

The cell

The cell is really like a mini body, breathing, growing and metabolising substances as well as moving, responding to stimuli and reproducing. When a group of the same type of cells forms this leads to a specific type of tissue being created. This tissue then grows to form an organ that will continue to grow to make a system. When all the systems are joined a body is formed. The reproduction of a cell is carried out through the following processes:

Mitosis – there are five stages that must be completed before a new cell is duplicated from the original – prophase, metaphase, anaphase, telophase and the interphase (mnemonic **P**lease **M**ake **A** **T**ext **I**mmediately).
Here is a simple breakdown of what happens in each phase. The details can then be added once the basic idea is understood.
Prophase – preparing the cell for the reproduction process, the spindle is set at each end of the cell.
Metaphase – the middle of the cell is focused on when the chromosomes can be seen facing each other in the centre of the cell.
Anaphase – attachment to the chromosomes takes place by the spindles, one side is the original chromosomes the other the duplicated set. Each set is pulled to either end of the cell by the spindles.
Telophase – this is the terminal phase when all organelles are replaced in their position in the cells before division takes place and the process terminates.
Interphase – This is the resting or 'in-between phase', waiting for the process to begin again.

Each phase has to complete successfully before the next phase begins to ensure the duplicated cell is a perfect copy.

Meiosis – this process takes place in the sex cells, contained in the ovaries and testes. The number of chromosomes need to be reduced by half, ensuring that when an ovum and sperm join the total number of chromosomes in the cell is 46. This cell is called a zygote, and will divide through the process of mitosis, developing different tissues and organs at each stage and finally turning into a baby.

Mitosis is the process of duplication of the original cell for growth and repair.

Meiosis is the reduction process that takes place in the ovaries and testes, reducing the number of chromosomes from 46 to 23.

Complete the blanks in this table showing the functions of the organelles. You can check your answers on page 111.

Name of organelle	Function
Nucleus	
Nucleolus	
Nucleus membrane	Protects nucleus
	'Packages' proteins and lipids for use in the cell and transported outside.
Mitochondria	
	Transportation in the cell
	Produces proteins
Vacuoles	
Lysosomes	
	Jelly-like substance, organelles are suspended in this.
Centrioles	
	Part of mitosis, area where chromosomes line up in the middle of the cell.
Centrosome	

Tissues

Tissues have individual functions that enable the area to cope with specific processes. Look at the following list and fill in the appropriate tissue types:

Smooth linings ....

Ability to secrete ....

Ability to absorb ....

To remove particles, dust, etc ....

To protect from drying ....

To lubricate ....

To expand and contract ....

To be waterproof ....

To be able to transmit signals ....

To contract ....

To connect ....

To insulate ....

To support ....

To protect ....

To connect and protect ....

To transport ....

To be flexible ....

To absorb shock ....

Once you have successfully completed this exercise, use the worksheet on tissues on page 115 and complete the information for each tissue type. This will give different ways of revising this topic.

Skeletal system

Think about the strength of the bones, how they grow and what they are made of. This will give the basic information for the functions. When you are ready, complete the blanks in the following paragraphs.

Protects specific areas and gives .... and ....

Permits .... through attachment to ....

Production of .... in the red bone marrow.

Storage of ....

.... for the delicate organs of the body.

Content of bone
Compact bone tissue has .... for capillaries

and nerves to pass through this dense bone tissue.

Cancellous tissue can be found at the ends of .... and

is the only bone tissue to contain ....

Bone shape

To complete a skeleton all the pieces have to fit and work together. There are five main categories. Complete the following sentences.

Long bones act as .... and examples of these are the

....

Strong and .... bones are found where little movement is

required. These are known as .... bones and examples

of these are ....

These bones are embedded in tendons, are small and ....,

and known as .... and examples of these are the

.... and ....

Bones of different shapes are known as .... and examples

of these are ....

Bones that protect are known as .... , and examples of these

are the ....

Using the blank skeleton provided on page 118 practise labelling the bones, then on a separate sheet practise naming their shapes.

Joints enable flexibility of movement and a variety of directions in which the body part can move around.

Fixed joints – these are been sealed by fibrous tissue, preventing any movement. At birth the skull is made up of several bones that fuse together completely by 18 months of age. The pelvic girdle consists of three bones that have been joined by fibrous tissue to form one piece.

Cartilagenous or slightly moveable joints – the vertebrae have a slight degree of movement due to the cartilage tissue that is on either side of the vertebra, above and below.

Freely moveable – synovial joints are specialised due to the lubrication produced by the joint and the range of movements possible. Synovial fluid is produced in the bursa of the joint, providing a smooth movement and preventing friction. The most common synovial joints are:

....

List the bones involved and where they are found

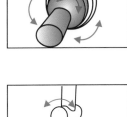

....

List the bones involved and where they are found

....

List the bones involved and where they are found

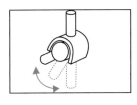

....

List the bones involved and where they are found

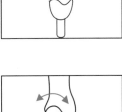

....

List the bones involved and where they are found

....

Postural deformities

Name the three causes for postural deformity:

1. ....

2. ....

3. ....

There are three main postural deformities.

1. This has an outward curvature of the spine, causing the neck to bend towards the chest. Name the curvature.

   ....

2. A lateral, sideways, curvature of the spine is know as

   ....

3. ....

   is an inward curvature of the spine causing the abdominal area to be pushed forward.

Fracture types

Define the following fracture types.

A simple fracture ....

Compound fracture ....

Complicated fracture ....

A bone that has had one end driven into the other..

When a bone shatters into several pieces it is a

....

Soft flexible bones have incomplete fractures known as

....

Muscular system

The functions of the muscular system are posture, movement and temperature regulation. Briefly list the explanations for each function:

Posture ....

....

Movement ....

....

Temperature regulation ....

....

Muscle contains …….. of water………..of protein, 5% of ….........., minerals ………. and glycogen.

Attachments are an important part of the connections supporting joints, giving flexibility and strength. A ……………. attaches bone to bone and a …………….. attaches muscle to bone.

Use the blank muscle diagrams on pages 116 and 117 to label the important muscle groups.

Blood

The functions of blood are:

P ....

M ....

T ....

Think about the contents of blood and use the quiz on the following page to test your knowledge.

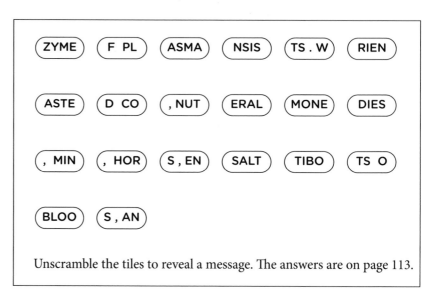

Unscramble the tiles to reveal a message. The answers are on page 113.

Cells of the blood

Fill in the gaps in the following statements.

Red corpuscles, known as ...., carry .... to the cells. They have a life span of approximately .... days.

White corpuscles are called .... Granulocytes form .... % of the white cells. The remaining white cells are .... which can be found in specialised tissue and monocytes that eat bacteria are known as ....

Platelets are also known as .... They are responsible for ....

Using the diagram of the circulation provided on page 119 label the heart, showing the flow of blood. Use a red pen to identify the oxygenated blood and blue for deoxygenated. Think about the layers of the muscular wall of the heart and fill in the gaps in the following statements.

The inner layer is the ...., consisting of epithelial tissue, ensuring the surface is smooth for the .... of the heart.

The middle layer is the thickest consisting of ....……..... . It is called .... The .... is the outer layer. Consisting of two layers, the inner is a ....

membrane, the outer is a fibrous structure keeping the heart in position.

The pulse can be described as the force of the blood on the …....…………

walls.

The cardiac cycle consists of three stages:

1. The ……….. contract forcing the blood into the ………………

2. The ………… relax and the ventricles contract pushing blood into the

……………………………… and pulmonary artery

3. The …………… leaves the heart and it relaxes before the next cycle.

Think about what factors can affect the heart rate.

1. ....

2. ....

3. ....

4. ....

5. ....

6. ....

Complete this table on the differences between arteries and veins. Think about the size and thickness of the walls, the content of the blood gas and the size of the lumen (passage). Also consider how the blood moves and how the waste matter is carried.

Differences between arteries and veins	
Arteries	**Veins**

Using the worksheets at the end of the book practise completing the tables and quizzes relevant to this topic.

The lymphatic system

The lymphatic system consists of a system of nodes that act as filtering stations. Label the nodes and the lymphatic tissue areas on the blank diagram for the lymphatic system on page 120.

This system is also known as the .... system, fighting bacteria as it enters our bodies, transporting excess fluid from around cells and inside tissues and ensuring any toxins are removed and digested through the network of nodes. Areas of lymphatic tissue in the small intestines are called ....,

and in the throat are called ....

Located behind the sternum is the .... lymphatic tissue. Attached to part of the ascending colon is the ....

The .... is known as the blood reservoir for the body.

The movement of lymph is assisted by the following;

- Contraction of .... muscles direct lymph towards the upper body

- The process of inspiration causes a pressure in the thorax moving lymph.

- Pressure from .... fluids assist in the lymph.

- Suction caused by .... pressure, due to close proximity to the heart, this pressure causes movement within the vessels.

The nervous system

There are three main parts to the nervous system. State what these initials mean:

CNS ....

PNS ....

ANS ....

What protects the brain and spinal cord? ....

How many pairs of cranial nerves are there? ....

How many pairs of spinal nerves? ....

A network of nerves is called a ....

What is a nerve called? ....

Nerves are protected by a covering called ....

The brain has many different parts. Find their names from the jumbled words below and then state the main function of each.

Mucbellere   Brecmue   Spons Ravoli

Demallu Goblatona   Potashylamhu   Dim Nabri

Part of brain	Function

Complete the boxes in the table below for the effects of 'fight or flight' on the body systems. What happens to each part of the body and what reactions does it show?

Effects of 'Fight or Flight'		
Part of body	**Affected by sympathetic**	**Affected by parasympathetic**
Senses		
Cardiovascular		
Circulation		
Sugar levels in the blood		
Respiratory		
Liver		
Adrenal glands		
Digestive system		
Excretory systems		

The endocrine system

The endocrine system works closely with the nervous system. Messages are received from sensory receptors concerning the environment and any changes that occur in it. The hypothalamus sends any relevant information to the pituitary for glands to produce hormones that may be required for the body to function correctly. Hormones are the chemical messengers that travel to the relevant glands taking the information to produce the hormones to support the body's growth and development.

This system enables the body to cope with day-to-day stresses, breaks down food as part of the digestive system, and assists the body to develop and prepare itself for different stages of growth.

The pituitary gland is the system controller. If it malfunctions it may send out too many instructions, causing a gland to overproduce a hormone (hyper), or send out too few, causing the gland to underproduce (hypo). Either of these can have negative effects on our health, potentially leading to serious conditions or diseases. If there is a problem with the pituitary gland the whole system will suffer and the body will need assistance to stimulate the endocrine system.

The glands may not be able to produce their hormone due to damage or degeneration. This can be remedied by drugs, for example the thyroid gland produces thyroxin, which can be given in the form of a tablet.

The stages for which this system prepares the body are:

1. Puberty
2. Menstruation
3. Menopause

Think about the glands involved in each of these stages and the hormones that are produced.

	Glands and hormones involved
Puberty	
Menstruation	
Menopause	

Using different coloured pens label the endocrine body on page 121 with the names of the glands and the hormones which they produce. Divide the body into sections and revise the glands and their hormones and functions and the effects of hypo- and hyper-secretion.

Some glands have several parts, each producing hormones. The adrenal gland is divided into two parts – the cortex and medulla. The pituitary also has two parts – the anterior (front) and posterior (back) each producing a hormone that is sent to glands in the body to initiate the production of their individual hormones.

Pituitary gland	Hormones produced	Function of hormones	Hypo secretion	Hyper secretion
Anterior	1.			
	2.			
	3.			
	4.			
	5.			
	6.			
	7.			
Posterior	1.			
	2.			

Before moving on to the glands of the body make sure that you understand the pituitary's function as the system controller, transmitting the messages for when to produce a hormone and how much to produce.

Take time between each section, have a break and let each chunk of information sink in before making a start on the next section.

Gland	Hormones produced	Function of hormones	Hypo secretion	Hyper secretion
Pineal				
Parathyroid				
Thyroid				
Thymus				

Gland	Hormones produced	Function of hormones	Hypo secretion	Hyper secretion
Pineal				
Parathyroid				
Thyroid				
Thymus				

Gland	Hormones produced	Function of hormones	Hypo secretion	Hyper secretion
Adrenal cortex	1.			
Adrenal cortex	2.			
Adrenal cortex	3.			
Adrenal medulla	4.			
Adrenal medulla	5.			

Gland	Hormones produced	Function of hormones	Hypo secretion	Hyper secretion
Pancreas				
Testes				
Ovaries				

The digestive system

The function of this system is to break down foods into their smallest molecules, enabling the body to absorb these chemicals at cellular level. The process begins in the mouth and ends with the excretion of the waste products via the anus.

The stages of digestion are:

- Ingestion (mouth)
- Digestion (stomach, duodenum jejunum ileum, pancreas, liver, gall bladder)
- Absorption (small intestine)
- Excretion (colon, rectum, anus)

The breakdown processes for each food type can be followed through the digestive tract, or alimentary canal, until the smallest molecule has been reached for that food type. Use the table on the next page to discover where each food type is broken down and what substance is used. The mouth is done for you as an example.

The villi are finger-like projections that cover the surface of the small intestines. They have a large surface area and are able to absorb the digested chemical foods. These are passed into the capillaries and taken into the circulation around the body to cellular level. The villi have lacteals that are lymphatic capillaries and absorb the fatty acids. They then become part of the lymphatic system before rejoining the circulation.

Large intestine

The functions of the large intestine are:

1. Absorption of: 1 ....
2 ....
3 ....
2. Secretion of ....
3. The rectum stores ....
4. The removal of wastes is known as ....

Organ or area	Enzyme, hormone, chemical	Action on substance	Result
Mouth	Salivary amylase	Works on starches to reduce size of molecules	Polysaccharides
Stomach	1.	In infants produces curds from milk.	
	2. Pepsin	Neutralises bacteria	
	3.		
Liver/Gall Bladder			Emulsified fats
Pancreas	1. Trypsin		
	2.	Fats	
	3. Amylase		
Villi (Inside			Monosaccharides
Small intestine)	1. Maltase		
	2.	Disaccharides	
	3. Lactase		
	4. (enzyme)	Works on Trypsin	
	5. Peptidases (enzyme)		

The intestines contain bacteria which protect the body and which are essential for a healthy digestive system. Use this table to revise the functions of the liver.

Removes	1.
	2.
	3.
Stores	1.
	2.
	3.
	4.
Produces	1.
	2.
	3.
	4.
	5.
	6.
	7.
Changes	1.
	2.
	3.
	4.

The pancreas is associated with the digestive and endocrine systems, producing enzymes to break down food molecules and the hormone insulin that regulates blood sugar levels.

There are many conditions and diseases that are linked with this system. As a result of the complicated processes involved there are various conditions that can develop, ranging from simple heartburn to irritable bowel syndrome.

The respiratory system

This system is responsible for drawing air into the body and passing oxygen into the bloodstream to be delivered to the individual cells. Using the blank diagram of the respiratory system provided on page 123 label the different parts of the system.

The passage of air. Fill in the blanks to complete the process.

1. Air is taken in by the .... and ....
   Here it is ...., ... warmed and moistened.

2. The .... is part of the digestive and respiratory systems, it warms and .... the air as it passes through.

3. The voice box, or .... produces the voice and .... the air.

4. The .... consists of a long tube that divides before entering the lungs. It has a specialised membrane with .... to prevent dust particles from entering the lungs.

5. Before entering the lungs the trachea branches into two parts called the ....

6. Inside the lungs the tubes reduce in size and become .... At the end of these branches are the ....

7. Alveoli is where the .... takes place. Capillaries on either side of the membrane transport the 'goods' to be exchanged.

8. The pulmonary .... brings deoxygenated blood from the heart to the lungs.

9. Pulmonary .... take oxygenated blood from the lungs to the heart.

10. The .... pushes the blood from the left ventricle enabling the blood to be distributed to the body.

How do gases exchange?

This is a method of transport called………………………………, when one side of a membrane has a higher concentration of a gas, and moves to a lower concentration. The capillary arriving from the heart to the lungs has a high concentration of carbon dioxide, while inside the alveoli the CO_2 concentration is low. The gas will 'move' to the lower concentration.

How do we breathe?

Chemical receptors (chemo receptors) are in position in the aorta and ……………… arteries, monitoring the levels of oxygen and carbon dioxide. When the level of oxygen drops or the level of carbon dioxide is too high a message is sent to the ………………………… and the diaphragm. This will cause the body to inhale and increase oxygen and decrease carbon dioxide. The ……………………… is responsible for initiating exhalation. The ………………… muscles and diaphragm are involved in inhalation and exhalation. The diaphragm ………………….. during inhalation, lowering the pressure inside the chest. The …………………………. muscles contract, raising the …………… . The capacity inside the chest is increased and air from outside rushes into the body.

During exhalation the diaphragm …………………… and becomes a …………………… shape raising the chest and reducing the capacity inside and forcing the air out. The ………………………...muscles relax causing the …………… to lower.

The urinary system

This system is responsible for cleansing the blood, removing the waste, controlling the balance of water, salt and potassium, assisting the blood pressure (BP) through blood volume and controlling the pH (acid/alkaline levels) and returning any substances that could be reused to the circulation.

The nephron is responsible for:

1. Filtration of blood
2. Reabsorption of materials required by the body
3. Formation of urine and excretion from the body

Label the blank diagram of the urinary tract on page 124. Then, using the table below, complete the different processes and areas.

Process	Substances involved and results of process	Area in which process takes place
Filtration		
Reabsorption		
Forming of waste and excretion		

The reproductive system

Complete the blanks in the following sentences.

The process in the male reproductive system requires that ……………….. is released from the testes. In order for this to happen …………………. ………....................………… is required together with ……....................…… …………………………….. to release the sperm from inside the testes. The sperm travels up the …………………………………. , along the ……………………………………., and passes through the …………………………….. gland. Here secretions are added to the sperm to ……………………………………. and aid …………………………….. . The resulting fluid is called ………………………….. . This continues the journey into the …………………………………… tissue of the penis to be ejaculated into the vagina. Here the sperm will swim up the ………………………………. into the …………………………… and up the ……………………………………………………………………. in search of an………....

The ovaries store eggs in the ……………………. ready to be released when initiated by the follicle stimulating hormone (FSH) …………………………... . The hormones ……………………………….. and ……………………………………………. are responsible for preparing the ……………………………... for the implantation of a fertilised ……………………………………………., also preparing the ………………………………………….. for production of milk.

The first sperm to reach and impregnate the ovum fertilises it, resulting in a ……………………………..., the first fused cell of a sperm and ovum. The total number of chromosomes for this fused cell is ………………… chromosomes, half from the mother and half from the father. The reduction process called ………………………………………… had taken place in the gonads to ensure the total number when a sperm and ovum joins is …………………….. pairs or ………………… chromosomes. The process of mitosis then begins, resulting in a morula, or mass of cells, continuing to develop and grow into an embryo, a foetus and finally a baby.

Think about the importance of the production of hormones responsible for the reproductive organs. Without these present no male or female reproductive cells would be able to join and create a new life.

The skin

Look at the blank diagram of the skin on page 126 and label as many parts as you can.

The skin has many functions:

1. Retains warmth and reduces cold in the body

    ....

2. Provides information regarding heat, cold and pain

    ....

3. Waste products can be

    ....

4. Selected substances can be

    ....

5. .... is given against bacteria and UV rays of the sun.

6. To keep the skin supple sebum is ....
    from the skin.

7. Ergosterol is activated by the UV rays and ....
    is produced.

Label the blank diagram of the skin on page 126 using a different coloured pencil or pen for each layer. The epidermis consists of five layers. Here are some clues to help you fill in the blanks.

		Functions
C		1. Desquamation
L	or clear	1. Only found on palms and soles
G		1. Cell membranes are dying
S	or prickle cell	
G	or basal cell	

Dermis – specialised cells

.... are responsible for the production of collagen,

elastin and areolar tissue.

Responsible for the production of histamine and heparin are the

.... cells.

Leucocytes fight ....

Sensory receptors – take information to the brain regarding changes to protect and defend the body.

Sweat glands – there are two types. These are activated during puberty and can be found in the axilla and groin areas.

They are called ....

Hair follicles – each hair has a tiny muscle attached called

....

that assists in ....

When hair is pulled tight .... form on the skin.

Sebum is produced from the ....gland to

moisten the skin and hair.

There are many skin conditions and diseases that can result from poor diet, dehydration, lack of care and of course stress. Others can be hereditary, a result of trauma or over exposure to chemicals or the sun. Think about each category in chunks. Revise each category separately and do not look at all the conditions as a whole. List the diseases and conditions under the appropriate category:

Congenital
General category
Fungal infections
Bacterial infections
Viral infections
Pigmentation

2.3 Techniques and tips for remembering key points

Reading is an essential part of learning. We use different reading techniques for different purposes, depending on the type of reading material and the reason why we are reading it.

When we read a train timetable, a map or warning notices we are gathering information. When we consult manuals, read how to construct flat pack furniture or look at a cooking recipe we are reading instructions. Reading for study could involve research, learning a language or revising, whilst reading for pleasure could be the latest novel or magazine.

There are alternatives to straightforward reading, such as skimming. We use this technique when we want to gather information quickly by running our eyes over a page to get a rough idea of its content. Scanning is a similar technique to skimming. Scanning can be used to locate specific information without having to read every word. It can be useful when reading a magazine, because you may not have time to read the whole article but require specific information from it. Just as there are different ways to read, so there are different ways in which to study. Here are some examples:

Annotations
For theoretical content you can enlarge the piece of work and annotate it in different colours to indicate different types of content.

Cue cards
Notes or cue cards are always handy for revision. You can list definitions or write key words from which you can fill in the gaps.

Flashcards
This invaluable tool remains one of the best and most popular techniques for memorising information. You can use index cards and write one question on one side and the answer on the opposite side. These can be useful for self-testing or asking a family member or friend to test you. Adapting the flashcards for study groups can be an alternative and fun way of learning. Try making a matching game with the cards. Make separate cards for the questions and the answers, leaving the reverse side blank. Place the cards face down and turn them over one by one to locate the pairs.

Mind maps

Mind maps are excellent tools as they simulate the working of the brain. For many students making mind maps is more interesting than making conventional notes and because of this your brain will find it easier to memorise the information. Mind maps consolidate what has been taught in the lesson and can embed the information by linking it to the subject. For anatomy and physiology this can be very useful for helping to understand the inter-relationship of each body system.

How to draw a mind map

Like the map shown at the beginning of the book start with one central idea on a landscape piece of paper. Then branch out from the idea with the main aspects which link to it, connecting them with arrows. Use lots of colour, underlining and pictures to aid the memory process.

Mnemonics

These are rhymes of any kind that will help us remember information. Relating the information to something the student finds humorous or interesting will help to embed it more firmly. Here are some examples of mnemonics:

1. The bones of the **upper limb**
'**S**ome **c**ooks **h**ate **u**sing **r**ough **c**uts **m**aking **p**ies'
(**s**capula, **c**lavicle, **h**umerus, **u**lna, **r**adius, **c**arpals, **m**etacarpals, **p**halanges)

2. The bones of the **lower limb**
'**H**elp **f**rantic **p**olice **t**o **f**ind **t**wo **m**issing **p**risoners'
(**h**ip, **f**emur, **p**atella, **t**ibia, **f**ibula, **t**arsals, **m**etatarsals, **p**halanges)

3. The layers of the **epidermis**, depending on which names you need to learn.
'**c**lever **l**ads **g**et **s**uper **g**rades'
(stratum **c**orneum, stratum **l**ucidum, stratum **g**ranulosum, stratum **s**pinosum, stratum **g**erminativum)

or

'**H**appy **c**heering **g**irls **p**erform **b**est'
(**h**orny, **c**lear, **g**ranular, **p**rickle cell, **b**asal)

Roman room

The Roman room technique is an ancient and effective way of remembering unstructured information. This method works by linking the information to recognisable images, in this case relating to objects in a familiar surrounding.

Imagine a room that you know well, perhaps your bedroom, or a dining room. Within this room there are features and ornaments or objects in known positions. The basis of this system is that things remembered are associated with these objects. For example, in the dining room I can visualise the following objects, a table, lamp, hi-fi, sideboard, candlesticks, chair, mirror, paintings, etc. When studying a system of the body try to relate these objects to the anatomical names.

Take the cell for example, when walking through the dining room door you could visualise a Golgi apparatus by the sideboard, on the table is a bowl of cytoplasm as your first course followed by two mitochondria and some vacuoles. Dressing the table are two lysosomes with lighted candles. On the wall is a beautiful painting of an endoplasmic reticulum, etc.

Study buddy or study group

For students who like to talk through subjects and revisit particular areas a study buddy or study group can be invaluable. When revising with like-minded people, rather than a family member or friend, information can be stored more easily, as sometimes group discussion can lead to the answer. Regular meetings are also useful to stop procrastination and for ensuring that everyone in the group is kept on track.

Successful E-learning

E-learning allows flexibility with when and how to study. The computer has become as essential to successful study as the pen and paper. It can cover all learning styles, thereby appealing to all types of student. Here are examples of ways in which the computer can become part of your normal study strategy:

- Adapting word searches and crosswords
- Online quizzes
- Communication with the tutor (useful for missed lessons)
- Emails between students
- Finding information
- Interactive quizzes using diagrams
- Organisation – using an electronic diary for planning
- Keeping a copy of your work for later revision

- Designing quizzes or puzzles for study groups
- CD-Roms available on the subject
- Virtual learning environments, providing instant feedback from tutors.

2.4 Constant reviewing of information

Why is there a need to go back to the beginning?

When studying over a period of time, it is easy to move with the subject and get caught up in the topic of the moment, with little thought for the knowledge learnt at the beginning of the course. Bear in mind that it was the information you learned at the start of your course which has enabled you to get to where you are now. All those facts, details, diagrams and examples are part of the learning process.

Try to think of learning anatomy and physiology as being like building a wall – each brick is a piece of information about the subject, the cement is your studying and the plans are the tutor.

Without the plans the wall will not be built correctly and have no strength for another structure to be added. No bricks would mean no knowledge to be learnt and no further learning could take place. Without cement the knowledge would not be held in place, joining other knowledge and continuing to build.

Try to ensure that you have set times planned for revising the topics that have been covered, so that the details remain fresh in your memory and are easily retrieved. Think of studying as a complex puzzle that needs to be worked through in a series of stages. The first stage showed the way to solve the puzzle, and subsequent stages enabled you to move forward and develop, but sometimes in order to move forward you also need to look back.

The human body has many systems to learn and within each system there are numerous functions and processes to be understood. At the beginning these may seem overwhelming, with no guarantee that the whole picture will become clear as each system is discussed. However, by taking the time to revise the previous topics the parts of the jigsaw begin to drop into place and an area that seemed confusing can become clear and there is a 'Eureka' moment.

Each system inter-relates with the others, assists in processes, provides materials, removes waste matter and provides protection and support. As each system is covered this interdependency becomes clear and the reason for certain structures and processes to be in place are obvious.

Brain fade

There is another reason for constant reviewing – brain fade. This can happen when a subject has been learnt and stored away in the long term memory, and not recalled or discussed for some time. The brain's memory begins to 'fade' on that particular information. Like a file of data lost at the back of the cupboard, it cannot be found easily. The processor struggles because there is no recent recall marker to assist in retrieving the information. This link or wiring in the brain has to be used from time to time to strengthen the connection and refresh the memory – it is a case of use it or lose it.

SECTION 3
REVISION PLANNING

3.1 The value of study buddies and study groups

The value of the sessions

Some people find it difficult to study alone, and benefit from the support of a classmate, or a group of fellow students. The value of studying within a group should never be underestimated. These sessions can be of immense benefit as they enable the topic to be discussed, with different opinions put forward, development of the subject and embedding of knowledge. However, this can only be achieved when all members of the group are on the course, or have taken the course in the past, as specific knowledge of the subject is required to participate in the discussions, give opinions, and offer individual research and knowledge.

Family members can be useful as testers, using a set of prepared flash cards with the questions on one side and answers on the reverse to test knowledge. This method works very well, providing the answer given is exactly as stated on the card. If it isn't, this can lead to frustration as the tester may not be able to determine whether an answer is correct or not, or how far short it is from being the perfect answer.

When working with a fellow student, their existing subject knowledge will enable them to elicit further details, or give hints about the areas not covered in your answer, encouraging more details to be given. Working with fellow students helps to create an air of camaraderie in which you can discuss any concerns you may have about not being able to cope. Knowing that others feel out of their depth as well stops you from feeling isolated and helps to build a bond to learn together and master the most difficult topics.

While some people find it difficult to study alone, others prefer it. These people are usually self-disciplined, able to manage time efficiently and prioritise without the need to consult others.

Some people are shy, or embarrassed about their lack of knowledge, or what they perceive as their lack of their knowledge, and as a result prefer to work alone. Remember that people are on a course to learn, if they knew everything already they wouldn't be there. Sometimes the people who talk the loudest can be just as concerned as those who remain quiet. By teaming up with another member of the course, or a group, to revise the topics you gain a number of advantages. These are:

- companionship
- joint targets
- set times
- organisation.

All these subjects will be covered later in this section.

Each learner has their own way of revising, this has to be identified and used to achieve the best results. One of the main advantages of studying in a group is that areas of weakness can be highlighted and subjects identified for future revision sessions.

Organisation

Every successful business has a plan to ensure that progress is made. Teams are created to handle specific tasks to ensure that time and resources are not wasted by several people doing the same tasks. This requires leadership, tasks being designated for the team, a realistic time frame to achieve these objectives and a set format for meetings to take place.

Organisation is the key to successful study, especially when it involves more than one person. Without an organised framework the session will not achieve what it set out to do, discontent will result, and eventually attendance will diminish and the group will break up.

Each study session needs a group leader – this can be the same person each time, or members can take it in turns to lead the group. Their responsibility is to ensure the smooth running of the session, with effective time management, achievable goals and a conducive atmosphere for the duration of the study session.

Time management

Time is what we want most, but what we use worst. William Penn

Time can easily slip through our fingers. What starts off as a few moments spent chatting can easily become thirty minutes and then an hour. Unfortunately we can never reclaim this time and study time is precious and needs to be used in the most effective way. The group leader needs to manage the session, be able to chart progress made against time passed and prevent the group straying from the topic. A break needs to be constructive – still part of the session, but enabling the group to have a chat and then return refreshed and ready to proceed with the revision. The end of the session is just as important as the start.

The beginning of the session should include an outline of exactly what will be covered and how it will be achieved. The end of the session should include a check to ensure that specific aims have been achieved and that each group member is happy. This phase should not be left until the very end as this will cause the proceedings to be rushed and could mean items are forgotten, or a person has no time to present their opinions.

Achieved aims

The aims of the session require thought and discussion. This should take place before the session, at the same time as selecting a leader. All members should have an input into the discussion topics, and any tests that may be suggested. The leader, once chosen, can then assign tasks to members to prepare for the session allowing time for each topic to be covered.

As an example, if the selected topics were the cell and tissues, the group would need to decide what the aims should be for each topic. The cell is a vast subject and requires specific study aims for each session, such as cell functions or names of the organelles. If the selected topic was tissues, the study aims could be locations in the body, and functions of the tissues.

All these topics are specific and achievable – a blank cell to be labelled, a worksheet for the functions, a blank body for tissue location and a worksheet for the functions of the tissues. This ensures that the session will achieve its aims within the allocated time, group members will want to return for another session and that they will be willing to prepare worksheets, or questions.

Specific topics need to be covered for each system, and may well be decided by the group. A discussion of weak areas could provide a list of topics to work through ensuring that all areas of concern to members are covered. The group leader would have the responsibility for organising sessions to cover all suggested topics in a variety of ways, e.g. multiple choice questions, charts, diagrams.

Some systems need to be divided into sections, or chunks, in order to manage the revision process successfully. The skeletal system, for example, can be divided into the following sections:

- Bone formation
- Skeleton parts
- Bones shapes
- Functions of the system
- Joints
- Deformities
- Diseases

As each system is worked through there needs to be a discussion on how it works, or links, with other systems and the functions they provide for each other. Build knowledge by retracing previous information, working backwards is another way of revising especially in a group, or pair, situation. The skeletal system could be the topic for one evening's study. For thirty minutes before the end of the session the group could discuss:

- How the skeleton is formed – spine, skull, ribs, etc
- How bone is formed
- The tissue type
- The categories of tissue
- Cell type
- The functions of the cell

This could be achieved through a question and answer session, with the answers being given by the members and books only being used when necessary. By learning this way the previous information studied is constantly reviewed and embedded in the long term declarative memory.

When all systems have been revised, plan a session concentrating on the linking and working of the systems. In a group, two systems can be given to each pair to discuss and present to the rest of the group what functions they do for each other. As all systems are discussed the whole group could then link them together using flipchart paper, establishing the network of processes that each system provides to enable other systems to function and their dependency on each other.

Atmosphere of the session

The session needs to be managed in a relaxed manner, enabling the group members to have an enjoyable session while still achieving their set goals for revision. If there is complete quiet and only the leader speaks, the relaxed atmosphere may be lost and the group members may feel uncomfortable, unable to participate, and feeling intimated. The session may then end up being a waste of time for many members of the group.

The leader needs to manage the session, without appearing to control it. A good facilitator is effective at time management without clock watching, keeping the group on task without being bossy and reminding them what the session is for without constantly repeating it.

The session may well take place in a member's home. If so, try to ensure that distractions such as the television or phones, are kept to a minimum. Try to encourage family members to either go out for the duration of your study session, or stay in another room to make sure that neither group is disturbed. Heating and lighting should be appropriate for the group size and planned activities. There needs to be adequate room for all members to sit and work comfortably and any equipment that may be required needs to be at hand.

Each session should include some fun elements, as learning can take many forms. Children play and do not realise learning is taking place. Adults can also learn in the same way. A kind of musical chairs game can be played to place the names of bones on a cardboard skeleton. As the music stops a name is taken from an envelope and placed in the appropriate place on the skeleton. The person who places the last one makes the tea or brings cakes to the next session.

Some groups may contain members who respond to quiet studious conditions, which will not suit other types of learners. Try to ensure that everyone's personal study requirements are met, giving a relaxed experience and achieving successful results.

3.2 Realistic targets

When enrolling onto a course, you will need to be aware of the course requirements and deadlines, in order to assess whether they are achievable. Each target set either by you or your tutor will differ from the last and may change throughout the duration of the course. You will be able to reach your goals by adopting realistic targets, staying focussed and planning ahead. When planning a study session you must first assess what you want to achieve from the session and then ask yourself 'can this realistically be done in an hour, or am I setting myself up to fail with unrealistic targets'. By breaking these down, however small they may be, into manageable targets you will successfully reach your goal.

> 'I've learned that everyone wants to live on top of the mountain, but all the happiness and growth occurs while you're climbing it.'
> (Andy Rooney, b. 1919)

When planning your revision strategy, try to follow the S.M.A.R.T approach, (specific, measurable, achievable, realistic, timed). If this is adopted the information will become embedded into the memory more easily, and at the end of the session the student will feel a greater sense of achievement and an ever growing confidence.

> 'If you don't know where you are going you will probably end up somewhere else.'
> (Laurence Peter, 1919-90, The Peter Principle 1969.)

Managing anxieties

Nowadays there is additional pressure on students to juggle commitments such as family and work in ways that were not expected in years gone by. More and more people are changing careers and studying later in life and colleges are aware of these additional anxieties. Students are having to become more creative in their problem-solving and more organised in their time management. In many establishments there are support groups available for giving advice on managing finance, grants, childcare, disability and many other issues that may arise for students. If you are experiencing difficulties in any of these areas, try to talk to the college early on and don't delay starting to resolve any issues. Tick any of the boxes below which may apply to you.

- ☐ Study and learning
- ☐ Finding time to do everything
- ☐ Understanding anatomical language
- ☐ Developing self-confidence
- ☐ Keeping up with classmates
- ☐ Meeting homework deadlines

Family, personal and work commitments
- ☐ Organising childcare
- ☐ Juggling finances
- ☐ Making friends in class
- ☐ Coping with studying and job requirements

Look again at the points listed above and put them in order of difficulty from 1–10, where 1 represents a minor problem which can be easily overcome and ten represents a major difficulty. Now take your findings and devise an action plan to fit in with your lifestyle.

Making an action plan

Resources
- Look at what resources are available to help you with studying. Contact the college.
- Form a study group or pair up with a study buddy.
- Identify your personal resources using a mind map with a central point, then brainstorm from there to identify home, college, home, and other help available.

Priorities

- What needs to be done first?
- Which areas can wait a while? Be careful of procrastination, don't put things off just because you don't like them!
- Place each subject area in an order of priority.

Reflection

It can help if you write down and explore why you are anxious about an area of study. Maybe you missed the class or it didn't interest you, therefore you switched off during the lecture.

- Write down how you feel about the specific system.
- Note your options and decide how you will tackle your revision.
- Make sure you keep a log of how you deal with each area of anxiety, so you can evaluate your progress later and see if you can solve another problem by using the same method.

Be aware of self-sabotage

Sometimes students inexplicably set patterns that they use in their daily life to sabotage their own best laid plans. At other times we fear failure so much, we just want it to happen quickly so that we can get it over with. Have you ever said to yourself 'I don't know why I am trying this because I know I can't do it'? Here are some examples of self-sabotage:

- Not attending classes, finding feeble excuses to avoid going back after a break. We all know that feeling of entering somewhere that we haven't been for a long time and having to explain why.
- Leaving work to the last minute and cramming study until the early hours before an exam.
- Filling the time with anything except study.
- Not turning up for an exam because we have convinced ourselves that we will fail anyway so what's the point?

Expect the unexpected

With careful planning and an effective action plan you can prepare yourself for the unexpected. During the course you will inevitably have some reason such as an illness or a holiday for not being able to attend class or do your homework or revision. If you plan ahead and keep on top of your revision and homework schedule you are less likely to be phased when the unexpected occurs.

Relaxation

In addition to the points above remember to build into the timetable some 'me time'. Don't feel guilty if you take the day off and do something enjoyable with the time. Remember a fresh mind is a productive mind! On the next two pages are a blank timetable for revision and a completed example. Please note Sunday has been left free for flexibility and time out.

Planning and preparation is vital for any revision session to be successful. To plan a dinner party there are many elements that need to be put in place, food to be bought, etc. The order and timing hold the key to success.

Revision planning can be thought of in the same way, carefully choosing the items to be discussed in a chronological order.

There is also a need to discuss and recap what has already been learnt, embedding the interlinking workings of the systems.

Suggested agenda for revision session on joints

Identify the categories
1. Synovial joints (freely moveable) – think about the make-up of the synovial fluid and note the joints within this category and their location within the body.
2. Cartilagenous joints (slightly moveable) – note the joints within this category and their location within the body.
3. Fibrous joints (fixed) – note the joints within this category and their location within the body.

The following pattern should be considered at the end of each revision session:

Retrace the origins

- Joints are formed through bones either fusing or being joined by cartilage and ligaments.
- They are joined to the mainframe of the skeleton.
- How is the skeleton formed?
- How are bones formed?
- What is their tissue type?
- How are tissues formed?
- Are they living?
- What are their requirements for growth and repair?
- What are the systems for waste removal?
- What happens when things go wrong?

Systems	Monday	Tuesday	Wednesday	Thursday	Friday	Saturday	Sunday
Cell	20 mins						R
Tissues	20 mins						E
Skeletal		20 mins					L
Muscular		20 mins					A
Cardiovascular/Lymph			20 mins				
			20 mins				X
Nervous				20 mins			A
Endocrine				20 mins			T
Digestive					20 mins		I
Respiratory					20 mins		O
Urinary/repro						20 mins	N
Skin						20 mins	

Systems	Monday	Tuesday	Wednesday	Thursday	Friday	Saturday	Sunday
Cell							
Tissues							
Skeletal							
Muscular							
Cardiovascular/Lymph							
Nervous							
Endocrine							
Digestive							
Respiratory							
Urinary/repro							
Skin							

3.3 When and how to prepare for the exam

When to prepare for the exam

The thought of preparing for examinations can cause increased stress on both the students and all those supporting them. In any area of life success is much more likely if we are well prepared, thoroughly organised and have allowed sufficient time for the task in hand.

Planning a complicated event, such as a wedding, in a week would be impossible, but with sufficient time and effective planning, success could be guaranteed. The planning and organisation of revision should be considered in a similar way. Timing the lead up to important deadlines or mock exams is essential, ensuring that no preparation is rushed, shortened or cut from the plans.

Ideally, revision should be planned into your daily routine from the moment the course begins. This will reduce your stress levels as exam day approaches, as you will have been continuously revising topics for some time and the subject matter should be fresh in your mind.

Cramming

Cramming is not advisable as it can inflict a great deal of stress on the body, does not ensure all the facts are retained and can cause the student even more worry as their lack of knowledge becomes apparent.

To try to cram all the necessary facts for all the systems of the body, their functions, processes and locations, would be a daunting task and would not instil confidence when preparing for the exam.

When cramming, people frequently study into the early hours of the morning hoping to cover all the subjects and get an overview of how all the systems work. To be able to perform well in the exam, all systems should have been studied several times in addition to the ways in which they inter-relate and complement each other. This cannot easily be achieved by cramming.

When this does become necessary ensure these points are adhered to:

- Set the timer
- Relax
- Set the sessions for 20 – 30 minutes then relax for at least an hour.
- Do not miss a meal or fluid intake.
- Do not revise until late into the night.

Make sure you complete your revision before normal bedtime.

In conclusion, remember that preparation for the exam actually starts the day the course begins and continues for the duration of the course until a few weeks before the exam.

How to prepare for the exam

The prospect of an imminent exam can be extremely stressful for some students, regardless of whether they have a successful track record in taking exams. Understanding the reason behind the exam can contribute towards your success and having some control over the process can help create a positive mindset, which is crucial for the exam experience. In order for a study session to be effective you will need to plan and organise your revision not only to fit in with your lifestyle but also who or whatever happens to be around you at the time.

Firstly, with the help of the earlier sections of this book, establish which learning style is right for you – it could be using mind maps, flashcards or a variety of the suggested methods. Would you benefit from working in a group or on your own? If working in a group or a pair is appropriate for you, make sure that each session gives you what you want. Try not to fall into the trap of staying in the group just because the members are your friends. For a study buddy system to be successful you need focus and organisation. There is always the danger that it might turn into an 'elevenses' meeting. You should also ensure that this is the right process for you – if you are in a group with someone who is disruptive, it could be your study that suffers. Remember that it is is your responsibility to take control of your own revision and by doing so you will be much more likely to succeed.

SECTION 4
EXAM PREPARATION

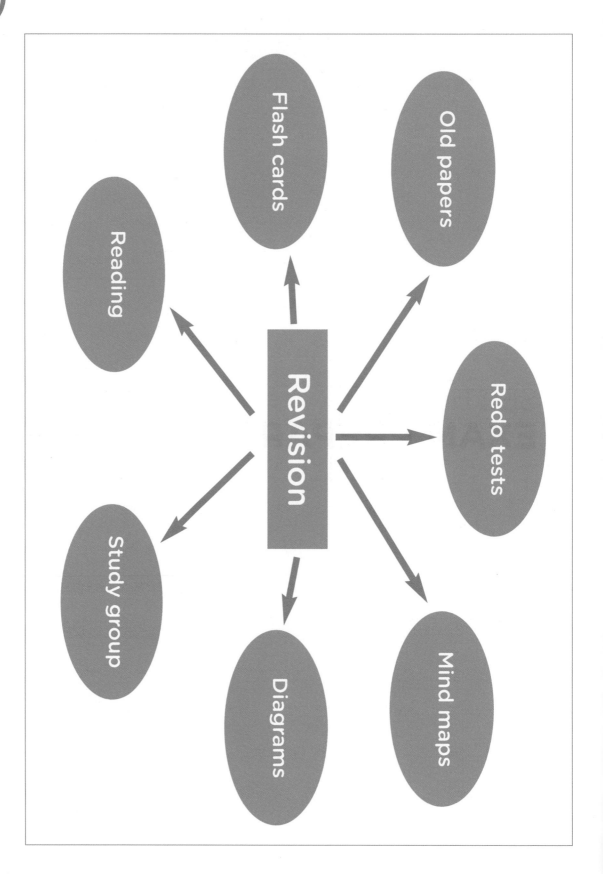

4.1 Techniques for taking exams

Multiple choice

Using specific techniques designed for multiple choice examinations will ensure that you don't panic or waste time unnecessarily and will help you to achieve good results. These strategies are devised to encourage you to focus on a routine to enable you to work through the paper, allowing adequate time for each question and time to re-read the paper before the end of the exam.

Think about how you are going to feel when you take a multiple choice exam. You will probably feel anxious and stressed. A good way to reduce these negative feelings is to increase your confidence. You can do this by reading through the paper a couple of times, or even scanning it quickly. This gives an overall picture of the contents and highlights the questions that you can answer immediately.

The process of answering any easy questions first will have a calming effect and allow your brain to function at full capacity, instead of having to cope with being stressed. It may be that you can complete these easy questions in less than the allocated time. If that is the case you will be able to spend longer on the questions that need more 'recall' time to answer.

Take time to consider each question, breathe deeply and remember that the first answer that comes to mind is usually the correct one. If you are in any doubt leave these questions to the end, come back to them and consider them again. As a result of answering all the other questions on the paper, your brain will have started to work at a different level and you will be able to remember more facts than you had previously thought possible.

Any remaining unanswered questions should be attempted with an educated guess. Think around the subject and eliminate all possible alternatives, always remembering that time is ticking, so GUESS!

Timing is essential. Have a watch on your desk and make sure that you stick to the time allocated for each question. Don't be tempted to overrun and force yourself to move on to the next question when the time has passed. Make sure you also allow time for the following:

- to scan the paper a couple of times at the start of the exam.
- to answer each question as fully as possible.
- to re-read the paper and make final adjustments ten minutes from the end of the exam.

By following a set method and observing strict time management you will be able to achieve the following:

- use your exam time effectively.
- reduce anxiety and increase confidence.
- develop and increase information recall.
- manage time effectively.
- increase brain activity enabling the harder questions to be completed.

Consider these four stages for answering a multiple choice exam:

1. **Scan** – allow five minutes to scan the paper, establishing the questions that can be answered easily. This will enable you to get a complete picture of the format of the paper. Using a pencil mark the questions that will require more time to answer and estimate how long they will take. Use a piece of blank paper to cover the answers whilst reading the question a couple of times. Have an answer in your head before looking at the answers on the exam paper.

2. **Easy** – complete the questions that you know will only require the minute or two allowed. Do not worry about going with the first answer that comes into your head. It can be scary to start answering the questions – try not to let this happen, be brave and let your mind do the work. Remember that the answer is always in the question. Read the question carefully and underline any essential words with a pencil. Remember that the correct answer is on the sheet. If you go blank don't panic. Go on to the next easy question and relax, breathe and close your eyes for a moment.

3. **Harder** – These questions should be left until you have answered all the others. Your brain should be working at maximum efficiency by now and many answers will come to you that you were previously unable to think of, allowing you to complete the more difficult questions. If you are still having problems with any of the harder questions leave them until you have answered everything else and then go back to them. If by now you are running out of time, consider an educated guess – it is always better to guess an answer than to leave a question blank.

4. **Final** – This is the last chance to answer any remaining questions. Basically this is the time to guess. Allow 5–10 minutes to reread the paper, making sure that you have answered all the questions and do not need to make any changes. Make sure that your pen and pencil are on the desk before the invigilator announces the end of the exam.

- Time the paper as described by the tutor.
- Reduce test anxiety by completing the four stages.
- Know when and how to guess if necessary.
- Use a piece of blank paper to cover answer whilst reading the question.
- Finish the exam on time, with your pen on the desk before the time is up.

Remember with multiple choice you cannot ask the audience or phone a friend!

Written paper

When taking a written exam the approach is similar to that for the multiple choice paper. Read the whole paper through once to establish what questions are being asked and what is required to produce satisfactory answers. Consider the order of questions and the best approach to adopt to reduce anxiety and maximise your brain's ability to process the answers.

Order of answering – writing about a subject knowledgeably makes you feel confident and help you to believe that you can actually pass the exam. This will boost your morale, reduce your anxiety levels and ensure that you achieve the best results possible.

Amount of writing required – if the question asks for an answer to be given in one or two sentences, make sure that it is concise and to the point. Do not write an essay if it is not required!

What does the examiner want to know?

What exactly does the question ask? If an essay type answer is required youu should have had plenty of practise writing these during the course. Look at the questions above and then formulate the answer:

The beginning – what the topic is covering and what will be discussed.
The middle – this should contain the main information on the topic – explanations, processes and functions.
The end – this draws everything to a conclusion, ensuring that all relevant information has been included and summarises what you have said.

Leave the more difficult questions until the easier ones have been answered, making sure that you observe good time management. Be strict on the amount of time per question and move on even if the answer is not complete. Mark it with a pencil and return to it when you have finished all the others.

You should observe strict time-keeping throughout the exam, allowing 5–10 minutes at the end to reread the answers. Make sure that your pen and pencil are on the desk before the invigilator announces the end of the exam.

4.2 Timing and preparation

Have you seen checklists in the run up to Christmas to help you prepare for the big day? For example, eight weeks before December 25th make the Christmas cake, six weeks before order the turkey, etc leading right up to the night before. Sometimes they even giving you timings for the day itself to ensure that your Christmas dinner is cooked to perfection.

Below is a guided checklist to help you in your preparation for exam day, assuming you haven't been studying right from the very first lesson!

8 weeks before the exam
- ❏ Devise an action plan to fit with your learning style
- ❏ Organise your study timetable
- ❏ Arrange resources
- ❏ Sleep (you will not remember if you are tired)
- ❏ Increase water intake
- ❏ Relax
- ❏ Talk to peers
- ❏ Keep positive

6 weeks before the exam
- ❏ Evaluate your revision. Shall I try something different?
- ❏ Tick off areas as you cover them
- ❏ Identify areas of strength and weakness
- ❏ Are there any subjects I am avoiding?
- ❏ Identify mock exam procedure
- ❏ Relax
- ❏ Drink plenty of water
- ❏ Eat healthily
- ❏ Are you getting enough sleep?
- ❏ Talk to peers
- ❏ Keep positive

4 weeks before the exam

- ❏ Are you ready for your mock exam?
- ❏ Tutorials discussing results
- ❏ From the mock exam you will be able to identify areas of particular strength and weakness
- ❏ Learn from the mock results (the reason for the mock exam is to help with your revision and to encourage you to aim for higher grades)
- ❏ Keep positive
- ❏ Talk to your peers

2 weeks before the exam

- ❏ Check domestic or employment arrangements such as childcare
- ❏ Check your understanding and memory
- ❏ Revisit each area of study
- ❏ Keep motivated
- ❏ Plan for emergencies
- ❏ Relax
- ❏ Drink plenty of water
- ❏ Eat healthily
- ❏ Are you getting enough sleep?
- ❏ Talk to your peers
- ❏ Have a positive approach
- ❏ Arrange resources – pens, pencils etc.

1 week before the exam

- ❏ Find ways of maintaining your interest and motivation
- ❏ Double check exam details such as duration and timing
- ❏ Stay positive
- ❏ Avoid mixing with people who make you feel unsure or who are super confident or those who panic
- ❏ If you require childcare, try to arrange this from the day before the exam to allow you some free time.
- ❏ Keep your mind clear and focussed
- ❏ Go for a walk or run to remove excess adrenalin
- ❏ Drink plenty of water to avoid dehydration. This will result in lethargy and headaches.
- ❏ Eat healthily
- ❏ Are you getting enough sleep?

The day/night before the exam

- ❑ Double check exam details such as duration and timing
- ❑ Try not to worry
- ❑ Stay positive. You can do it!
- ❑ Avoid stressful situations
- ❑ Prepare your equipment – pens, ruler, water, snack, clothing
- ❑ Has the car got enough petrol or do you know the bus timetable?
- ❑ Have a snack before bed and maybe a soak in a relaxing bath
- ❑ Leave plenty of time to sleep

The day of the exam

- ❑ Make sure you have breakfast, to keep up your stamina. Slow release carbohydrates such as bread or cereals are good for this.
- ❑ Leave plenty of time for the journey. Plan for a delayed bus or train and roadworks or learner drivers.
- ❑ Check you have your equipment
- ❑ Do you have your student number?
- ❑ Plan to arrive as the exam room opens. It can take time to find your place.
- ❑ Avoid people who panic
- ❑ Stay focussed

4.3 Preparation for the day

Revision – make sure this is timed and schedule it into your routines. Set a timetable for when, where and how the sessions are to be set, ensuring all topics are covered and life can still be lived. Do not revise on the way to the exam. Leave your books at home.

Relaxation – whatever relaxes the mind and body. Consider a bath, massage, or simply a walk in the park. Fresh air is essential for clearing your mind. Do some exercise, it stimulates the circulation and assists the workings of the brain. Do this the night before the exam, or even on the morning of exam day. If possible, walk to the exam centre. This will help you to keep calm.

Time management – Time cannot be held back. Take control of your time and make sure that none is wasted. Try to arrive just as the exam room opens.

Water intake – ensure this remains constant as the brain requires a large amount in order to function at peak performance. Take a bottle of water into the exam and sip frequently.

Bananas – these are a great source of potassium and energy. Have one before going into the exam and take one to eat when the exam is over.

Writing supplies – take a supply of pens, pencils, a sharpener and erasers. Do not leave anything to chance, it is better to have too many than to be in need.

Watch those minutes – take a watch and put it on the desk so that you can check each stage is completed in time – reading, selecting easy questions, harder questions, reread the paper.

Rescue Remedy – for those whose nerves need a little extra assistance. This is a natural remedy from the Bach Flower range and is taken to calm and reduce anxiety. This should be taken for a few days leading up to the exam day. It can be taken under the tongue as drops or in spray form.

GOOD LUCK!

4.4 Post Mortem

After leaving the exam room you immediately start to wonder how you have done. Was the answer to question 3 correct? Was it a synovial joint or slightly moveable? There is always a great desire to get out the reference book and then to try and remember how you answered all the questions. The group gathers outside the exam room and there are screams of joy, tears of despair, and endless debate about the questions and what the correct answers may be.

Try not to take part in this Post Mortem of the exam. It will make some feel euphoric and others dejected. This is not a useful exercise at this stage. After a couple of days it may be useful to go back over your answers to see what you might have done differently. Resits are available if you need a second chance, so you should never despair.

4.5 Self-evaluation

Identify one area of study that you are particularly proud of. This could be a difficult topic that you have finally mastered or an area of study in which you have excelled. Using this table analyse your achievement in more detail and evaluate your progress. On completion of the table you will be able you to appreciate and value your achievements.

Ask yourself	Evaluation – The journey travelled
My achievements My progress, how have things changed?	
How do I know that I have achieved this? What evidence is there, e.g. positive feedback or marks increasing?	
How did I achieve my goals? What resource did I use or what strategies worked?	
What is the significance of this? Why are you pleased or proud of this, what have you overcome?	
Where do I go from here? How can I build on this success?	

4.6 What next?

FURTHER STUDY –
ANOTHER COURSE SUCH
AS REFLEXOLOGY OR
FACIAL ELECTRICAL
TREATMENTS

RE-SIT
CONSIDER
REVISION TIMETABLE

INSURANCE
COVER

EMPLOYMENT –
SALON, GYM, MOBILE/
HOME BASED

4.7 Celebration!

> You cannot teach a man anything;
> you can only help him find it within himself.
>
> Galileo Galilei

This quote tells us that everyone has the potential to achieve their dreams but needs help with the direction in which to find them. Education is a voyage of discovery for all of us, helping us to find our hidden abilities. The unlocking of these hitherto unknown skills can be the beginning of a complete change in direction for our lives.

Every achievement, no matter how small, should be celebrated by everyone involved. Otherwise there is no recognition of all the hard work and effort that has been put into the process, giving little or no value to the journey that has been travelled and all that has been achieved along the way.

To celebrate is to give status to the achievement, to record and publicly announce the event as a step forward in the journey of life. It will also help to encourage the learner and all his or her supporters to consider starting another course or taking on another challenge.

So remember, book a table at a restaurant, have a family gathering at home or simply open a bottle of wine. It doesn't matter what you do, as long as you do something!

If there is an award ceremony to receive the certificate or diploma, make sure that this is attended by family members and friends who have supported you throughout the course. Thank them all for their support, childminding, help with revision or for just simply being there.

> Life is a celebration of awakenings, of new beginnings, and wonderful surprises that enlighten the soul.
>
> Cielo

SECTION 5
WORKSHEETS AND REFERENCE MATERIALS

Worksheets to aid your revision

This final section of the study and revision guide will provide you with a variety of revision aids. There are word searches to encourage familiarisation with anatomical language. For more visual learner diagrams have been provided for a selection of systems enabling their structures to be embedded within the long term memory. Puzzles and quizzes have been devised to encourage thought provoking revision and a fun aspect to learning during group or study buddy sessions. Ultimately, the philosophy behind the making of the worksheets is to instill an element of fun whilst learning. Enjoy!

'People rarely succeed unless they have fun in what they are doing.'

Andrew Carnegie

Glossary

Antagonist	Opposing muscle to prime mover, supporting muscle's contraction.
Antibodies	Part of the lymphatic system, defending against bacteria and viruses in the body.
Appendicular	Comprises the shoulder and pelvic girdles that are attached to the arms and legs.
Axial	Main axis of the skeleton – skull, spine, ribs and sternum.
Blueprint	Held within the nucleus of a cell is the DNA of a human.
Cardiac muscle	Specialised muscle that has the ability to contract continuously.
Ciliated	Specialised tissue containing hair-like projections, designed to keep passages clear of dust & particles.
Cognitive	Relating to cognition, the mental act or process of acquiring knowledge
Cramming	Studying for exams at the last moment.
Desquamation	Shedding of skin from the corneum layer of the epidermis.
DNA	Deoxyribonucleic acid – blueprint of a human.
Electorencephalogram	Machine that records brain activity.
Enzyme	Chemical that initiates activity in the body.

Epiglottis	A flap that covers the oesophagus when breathing and the trachea when eating.
Erector pili	Tiny muscle attached to the hairs of the skin.
Erythrocytes	Red blood cells.
Heparin	Blood clotting agent.
Hormone	Chemical messenger that is carried in the bloodstream.
Hypothalamus	Situated in the brain. Passes messages to the pituitary regarding changes required in the body.
Involuntary	Muscles that are not under conscious control.
Lateral	To the side of the body.
Leucocytes	White blood cells
Mineral salts	Chemicals essential to the workings of the body e.g calcium salts for bone growth and repair
Motor nerves	Nerves that carry messages from the brain to the parts of the body required to respond.
Papilla	Found at the bottom of the hair root, ensuring blood supply and nutrients are received.
Peristalsis	Wavelike contraction causing food to be moved in the digestive tract.
Prime mover	Muscle that is performing contraction.
Sebum	Produced in the sebaceous glands to lubricate the hair and surface of the skin.
Synovial fluid	Fluid that lubricates the joints, preventing friction.
Thrombocytes	Platelets that are part of the clotting process.
Semi permeable membrane	Covering that 'selects' materials entering a cell.
Sensory nerves	Detect changes in the body and transmit information to the brain to be processed.
Voluntary	These muscles move under conscious control and enable movement.

Answer key for exercises

Page 30
mitochondria
endoplasmic reticulum
Golgi Apparatus
lysosomes
vacuoles
nucleus
nucleolus
centrioles, centrosome,
centromere
nucleus membrane, cell
membrane
filtration
diffusion
active
dissolution
oxygen, water, nutrients

Page 31
1. protective
2. diffusion
3. water, membrane, equal
4. dissolution
5. active.
6. filtration

Page 33
Names of skull bones
Frontal, Palatine, Vomer,
Mandible, Maxilla, Turbinator,
Lacrimal, Parietal, Sphenoid,
Occipital, Zygomatic,
Temporal, Hyoid, Ethmoid.
Nasal

Page 34
scapulae, clavicles
innominate
ischium, ilium, pubis
humerus
radius, ulna
8, 5, 3, phalanges, 2
tarsal, 5, 3, phalanges, 2

Page 35
biceps, triceps, biceps femoris
digestive, respiratory
agonist, antagonist
isometric, isotonic
isotonic (movement),
isometric (tension)
attachment
belly

Page 36
insertion
origin
oxygen
oxygen, nutrients, water, salts,
enzymes, hormones
motor
reduction
overuse

Page 37
muscle matigue
tendon
ligament
fascia

Page 41
left atrium, right atrium, left
ventricle, right ventricle.
superior vena cava, inferior
vena cava.
pulmonary veins
aorta
tricuspid
pulmonary semi lunar valves,
mitral
septum

Page 42
interstitial
subclavian vein
bacteria
cleansing

Page 46 (1)
the duodenum
the jejunem
the ileum
villi

Page 46 (2)
warmed
moistened
digestive
respiratory
moistens
ciliated
warms
bronchioles
alveoli
pleura
intercostal

Page 47
cortex
medulla
renal pelvic
nephrons
cortex
medulla
cortex
renal pelvic
ureters
urine
bladder
urethra

Page 48
zygote
follicles
Fallopian
ova
neck
muscular

Page 49 (1)
epididymis
coiled tube

muscular tube
erectile
23
flagella

Page 49 (2)
epidermis
dermis
fibroblasts
elastin

Page 50
eccrine
Apocrine
papilla
erector pili
sebum

Page 52 (1)
Nucleus contains DNA
Nucleolus produces ribosomes
Golgi Apparatus 'packages'
proteins and lipids for use in the
cell and transported outside.
Mitochondria – 'Power house'
of the cell.
Endoplasmic Reticulum –
transportation in the cell
Ribsomes produce proteins
Vaculoes – storage areas
Lysosomes – digestive system,
breaking downs wastes
Cytoplasm – Jelly-like
substance, organelles are
suspended in this.
Centrioles – part of mitosis,
forms spindles at each end of
cell.
Centromere – part of mitosis,
area where chromosomes line
up in the middle of the cell.
Centrosome – part of mitosis,
area where centrioles are held.

Page 52 (2)
Simple epithelial
Cuboidal epithelial
Columnar epithelial
Ciliated Epithelial
Stratified compound epithelial
dry
Stratified compound epithelial
wet
Transitional
Columnar
Nervous
Muscular
Areolar
Adipose
Bone
Lymphoid
Cartilage
Blood
Elastic
White fibrous

Page 53
Support
Posture
Movement
Muscles
Blood cells and minerals
Protection
Haversian canals
Long bones
Red marrow

Page 54
levers
femur and humerus
compact
short
carpels and tarsals
round
sesamoid
hyoid and patella
irregular
vertebrae
flat
sternum and scapula

Page 55
Ball and Socket – hip,
shoulder
Hinge – knee, elbow
Pivot – atlas and axis, cervical
vertebra
Saddle – thumb
Gliding – wrists

Page 56 (1)
Congenital
Postural
Hereditary

Page 56 (2)
Kyphosis
Sciolosis
Lordosis

Page 56 (3)
A break of the bone with no
tissue damage.
When the bone pierces the
skin.
When an organ has been
damaged.
Impacted fracture.
Communited fracture.
Greenstick.

Page 57 (1)
Posture – the muscular system
gives shape and posture to the
body
Movement – through the
attachment to muscles the
body is able to move.
Temperature control – When
the body is cold the muscles
are instructed to contract
(shivering) to increase
temperature. Muscles contract
to retain heat within the body
e.g erector pili muscles in the
skin.

Page 57 (2)
75%
20%
Fats
Salts
Ligament
Tendon

Page 57 (3)
protection
maintenance
temperature control

Page 58 (1)
erythrocytes
oxygen
120 days
leucocytes
75%
lymphocytes
phagocytes
thrombocytes
blood clotting

Page 58 (2)
endocardium
lining
cardiac muscle
myocardium
pericardium
serous
the force of the blood on the
artery walls.
atria
ventricles
atria
aorta
blood

Page 60
immune
Peyer's Patches
tonsils
thymus
appendix
spleen
skeletal

tissue
negative

Page 61
central nervous system
peripheral nervous system
autonomic nervous system
meninges
8
31
plexus
neuron
myelin sheath

Page 67
water
nutrients
vitamins
wastes
faeces
elimination

Page 69
nose
mouth
filtered, checked
pharynx
moistens
larynx
warms and moistens
trachea
cilia
bronchi
bronchioles
alveoli
gaseous exchange
artery
veins
aorta

Page 70
Diffusion
Carotid
Brain
Pons Varoli
Medulla Oblongata
Intercostal

Relaxes
Intercostal
Ribcage
Contracts
Dome
Intercostal
Ribcage

Page 72
sperm
follicle stimulating hormone
male luteinising hormone
epididymis
vas deferens
prostate
nourish
mobility
semen
erectile
vagina
uterus
Fallopian tubes
ovum
follicles
oestrogen
progesterone
oestrogen
uterus
ovum
mammary
zygote
46
meiosis
23 pairs
46

Page 73
temperature control
sensory
excreted
absorbed
protection
secreted
vitamin D

Page 74 (1)

mast cells

fibroblast

bacteria and infection

Page 74 (2)

eccrine and apocrine

erector pili

temperature control

goose bumps

sebaceous

Page 132 Skin quiz

1. – 8

2. – 4

3. – 10

4. – 7

5. – 11

6. – 6

7. – 2

8. – 12

9. – 3

10. – 1

11. – 9

12. – 5

Page 133 Mix & Match

– the digestive system

1 and 10

2 and 12

3 and 7

4 and 11

5 and 9

6 and 1

7 and 4

8 and 2

9 and 3

10 and 5

11 and 6

12 and 8

Page 134 Mix & Match

– the skeletal system

1 and 4

2 and 5

3 and 1

4 and 7

5 and 3

6 and 2

7 and 6

Page 135 Multiple choice

questions

The cell: 1D, 2D

Tissues: 1B, 2C

The skeletal system: 1A, 2C

The muscular system: 1B, 2C

The cardiovascular system:

1B, 2C

The lymphatic system: 1A, 2C

The nervous system: 1A, 2D

The endocrine system: 1B, 2D

The digestive system: 1B, 2A

The respiratory system: 1D, 2C

The urinary system: 1C, 2 A

The skin: 1C, 2D

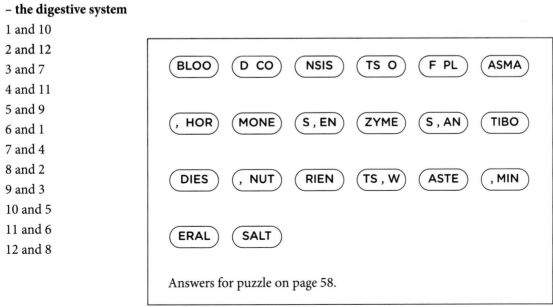

BLOO   D CO   NSIS   TS O   F PL   ASMA

, HOR   MONE   S , EN   ZYME   S , AN   TIBO

DIES   , NUT   RIEN   TS , W   ASTE   , MIN

ERAL   SALT

Answers for puzzle on page 58.

The muscular system (front)

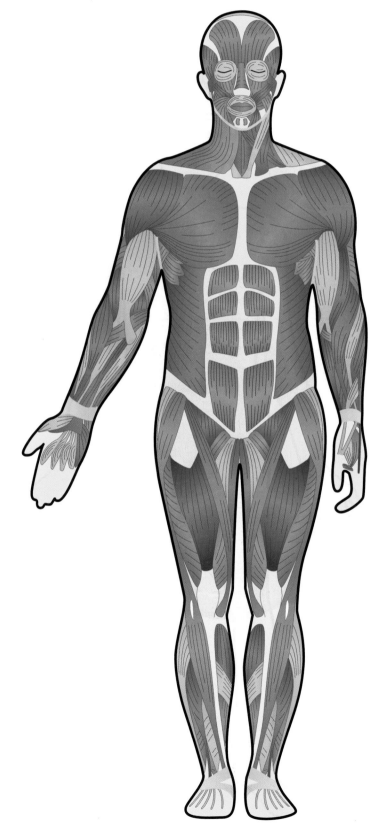

The muscular system (back)

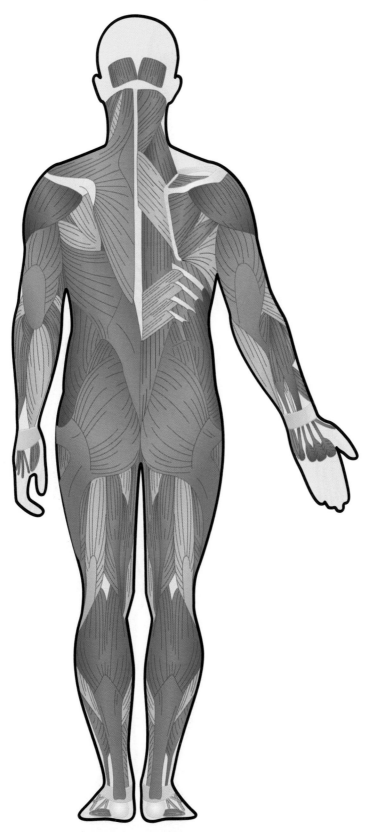

The skeletal system

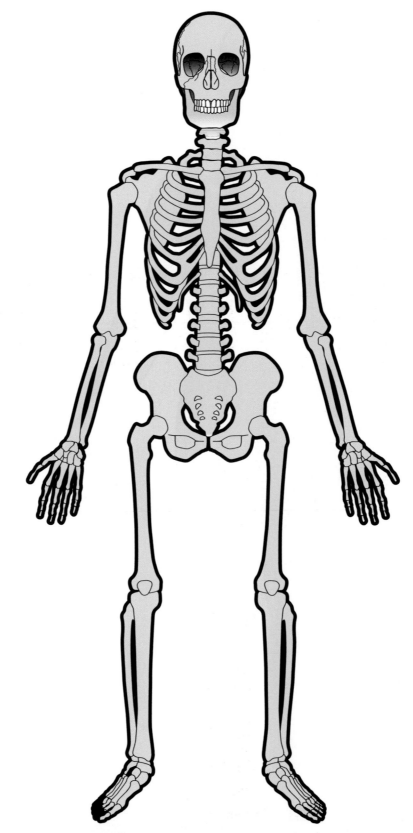

The circulatory system

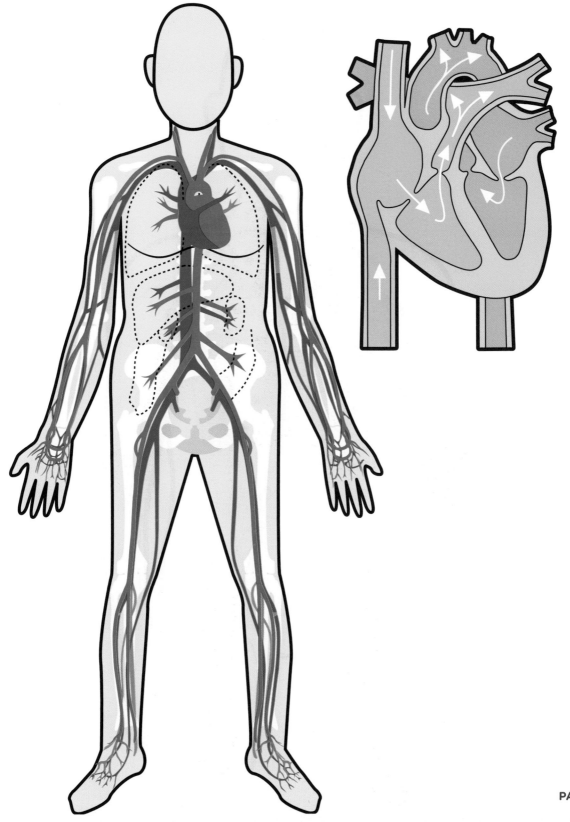

The lymphatic system

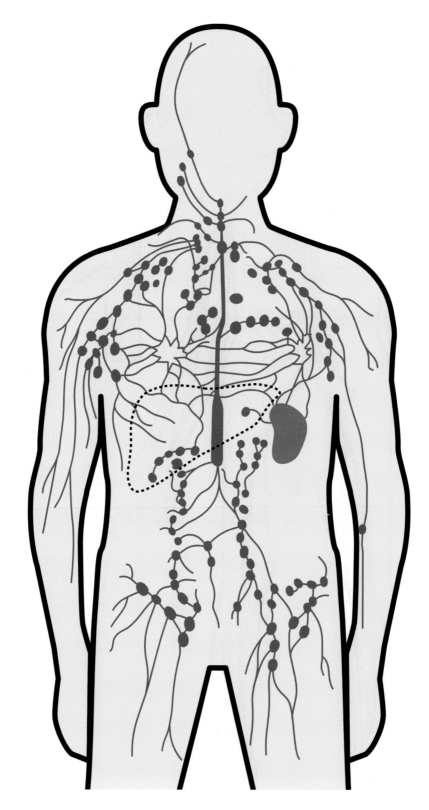

The endocrine system

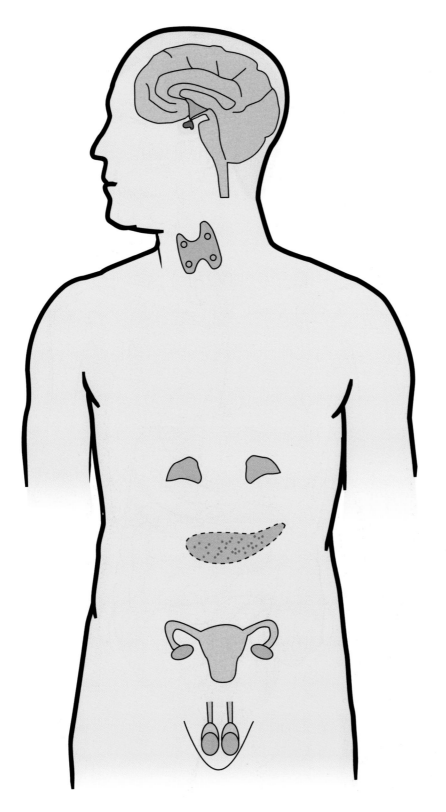

The digestive system

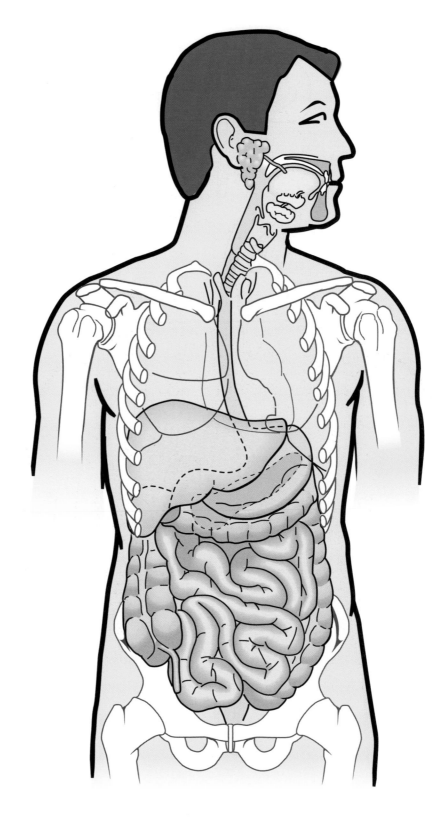

The respiratory system

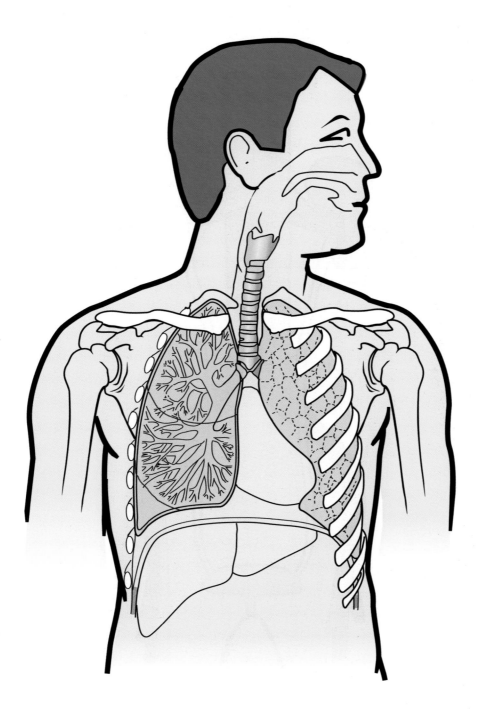

The urinary system

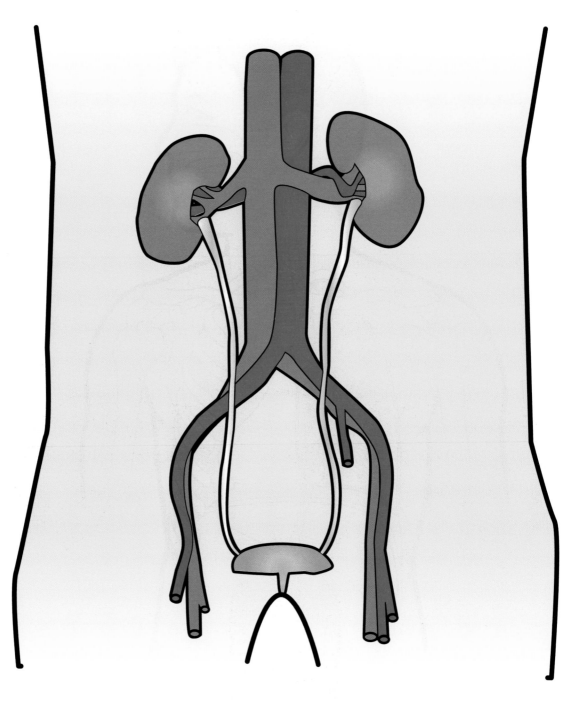

The reproductive system

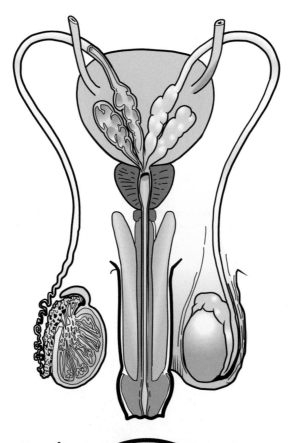

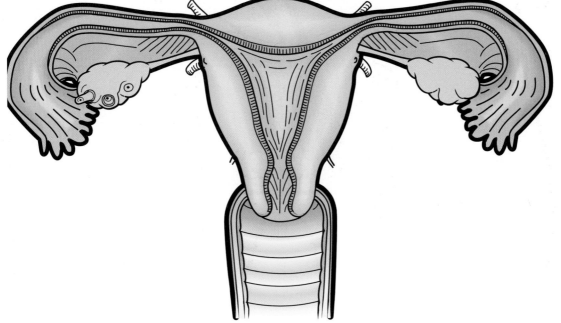

The skin

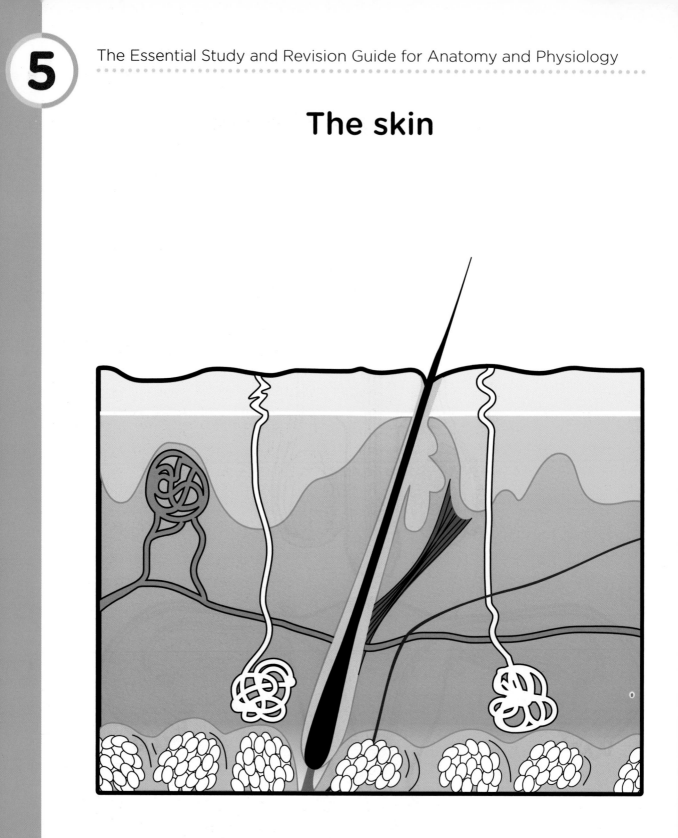

Wordsearch – the cell

nucleus	membrane	cytoplasm	mitochondria
vacuole	lysosomes	centrioles	cilia
ribosomes	centromere	centrosome	nucleolus
Golgi Apparatus			

```
S O M I   N U A A O T S A S H S E C L T Y V T S P G
T P P U O I   N P O O C L E T I   E R R I   A P S R M U
E S I   Y L P L E M L D C E R N L O T C L E A S L E
O P C E M C L S T L Y N R T R R E U A T I   I   O O O
M R L C L M A E Y T U A R I   O L O U A L M E E C N
N P G L P S U E O Y E I   R C O L N C I   R M T E L S
T T R A S M I   P N B O E G P E R E C B U E T L O T
I   A E S T S L L S L R E M S B N Y A S E O E T L P
T N Y E O A T T E E I   R E O A S C M B O N B P M C
S I   L C S R R S M O V T G R U E A U S O V N R R L
L C M M C E O O R S O E B T S S C C L P O I   C S A
S N M M   D R T L T R M A A I   L E E Y O B G P A C
R I   N O S T N M A A E R A L I   P U P C O L S T M O
L A O U N R O Y T M A E L E M R N E S O C M D S S
O P C E C M V R I   P S O M R S R D O R   M M O M U
S G C M P L C O P R P U C O U I   M N E S I   A S T L
S   S A O E E A M S B C M O S E I   A O O L L O I   E
L S S E S E   O U I   D O S R S O P S O H C P E E A
L L S O M I   N E L R A L O O E N R M E M C M C O E
E G A R G O L L O U E E E C N U S T O L S O U O S
O R S L G C S R E D S E U E P L I   N N E L B T L R
N O O B U M C O O A C A A T M O A T   E O M T I   P
I   G O N M   G H S M O E O S O O O S T E C O E L M
E M E O N S U E E Y G E P L O I   N M I   N R T T S O
T R S O O P T I   P I   L A E S E I   U C O A S S R B E
```

Wordsearch – the skeletal system

axial	appendicular	compact	cancellous
scapula	tibia	fibula	patella
femur	scaphoid	ulna	

```
E R E P P B P U D L L C O U M E A C N C T O A P X
M I A R U P L L T C L D C E A C A A F P C T L O A
E P X E P L T T C S P L U T U N N L A A N C E A F
A C T L R U S M A E I C A F C O N E D L U P A E O
C P D E C A B O A E L L C E U M X O L T U I M S U
M A A F T A C T A E T S L E B I I S I C I U C X M
D U P U I I D C U R C L A T P N I O N D R A L A F
D P U T A P E M A A O S E C A P F I A N P C C L C
P L H C S A B E P U E S A A S I S I P H T P I L N
L A L A A F L U S U E E A R B P U P O R L P F O O
L I F A T A L M B T T I A U A N E I E C N A L M U
P S M A L A A E T L N R L A I L D S R R E T N C R
M A L L A S A C N E O A A L S P U E L B L N S L D
P P L P P T L I T A I O D A O T P C P O F L C I U
T L P L A F U A A A I L P C L A A C I L U A T R A
P M P L C C N U C O P O P C A M N U F D R S S F B
S A P U I B T C C A R C I L B A P S L T N C A H L
O N T I L C O P A C A E A I C U L M P T L E A R C
A F P E A A A E I P A L F C N F E O C I I R P R L
P I C P L N L R U I E C O N T A A N T A C B L P A
A U M C A L U S L S L R A C L N B S P L L I I I A
A O S C N A A L T A U E U A I N O A C A R B A A L
C U A A O L F L P U C U L N I S L T I F A P P T A
I L E I L C C A L L A L S U A M C X S L U I A C T
P N P A E N E I A A E D N I M L A I A A H E A A S
```

Wordsearch – the muscular system

attachment	contraction	fatigue	glycogen
insertion	isometric	isotonic	lactic acid
ligament	muscles	nutrients	oxygen
tendon	tone		

```
C E C E E A C T U E I T O T F O N T X N E T T T E
O O C A G O U N G S C A O C R E I T O O I C E N C
S R C S T T N T I L E M C N C T I N F N N N Y E U
Y N I O I N F U O E Y T C N E I C E N T D U L M N
E T I I I X E T T R E C M S M T O C A O N A L C N
E R A G N E A M S R E E O S C N C S N D C T I N N
N L T I N C T G H E I G E G C L O R T T N C T N R
C T O T U C T G N C E E S M E I T I I U I I O N C
S S S E M L   R U L A N N C E N R C T N I C U O S
A E F T A O N E I T C T L T N T   T O R N T N F T
T C D C E N I N G I T L T G S A A T E N E T G O C
U O T N A X T T C R O N E A C T O T E M R S A E I
T O I O O I O O C N G O E I Y S I S E A O O N R I
F N E E E C C T M C A T D M I T L E C I I S C I I
O A T T E G M M N E N C A E A E G T U S O D I A M
S R T D C T N M G A N E Y E A G I N U T E L M U M
O E I I N O O N T T T N O N I O I E T O C A S L S
S T L L G C N E E E D I E I N E R L T C I C T C A
M A T A S U G O S H I G N N C M T O U A L C G S G
O E G N H L E A U T Y R G D N O C A E E T D N R O
T I S D S N I L N X I U O E D T T O S L R E I O I
X C H O N R M I O O L I E N M E O I E I T S O A G
N F N N N T D O I E G A E A G X T C S E R A I Y E
O D E U O I A A L S I E I C R T T N E T T O F L S
T T G N O R O O O I M T I T L R F T N O N I S T T
```

Wordsearch – the endocrine system

pineal	parathyroid	thymus	thyroid
adrenal	pituitary	pancreas	ovaries
testes			

```
A H L N R E N A A S R R E S T A T O P T A A S M N
Y R A E R E T S R T Y R P D T R O R S I R R R P H
C R Y Y T A I E E R A R A P R H R Y A O A P T Y O
L Y R R R Y D S S T I N U A N N P Y U Y Y T Y N D
R E E O Y A T R R Y S D E L D A S E L I L R V T H
L T P I O E E E E T T T V E P R A O P I N A S T E
T T D H S P E R Y N A R D A I T T R R R Y T A T U
R A O D H E T A A R A R H O C S S M A T Y A P S O
Y O D T O R R N E Y I L O P L T C N N H C A P A R
I R L P Y P L D T S A V L R S N P H R L A P H E R
A A R S I I P R I I N V O I I I E V P I I P L T S
E Y Y S R T A E N I E O P P U O R S Y N I N T R S
E S O P S T U A A E A M E A T T N U E Y T H R L Y
S A E S D A Y I T I E V A D R O D A T A R P P E I
T D O I S T E S T I S S T E S A L C U Y O Y M T I
R S A E R H E R R A E E L N N P T A D T T E R T S
A S R U I A T U C I R P O S U I N H N I R E H S M
R H U H N I V H R N E Y I I C O R R Y A R O O T S
R R Y M N T Y O Y Y A I A R E H P E H R T T R M S
R D R A Y T E A M R O P S O R E I A A A O S Y O U
H O S R C H S S L N O A A T I A O T A E C I T O T
L U E A S A T L E R A I I I Y R T T Y C T A D O A
A U E T V A S O I T I I D T E Y P H T T E N A D R
L N S A L T L E T A Y M R S R E H A A I A E T R S
I S R R Y T T U Y E I P Y A A V L R R R I T V E Y
```

Wordsearch – the respiratory system

alveoli	aorta	bronchi	diaphragm
epiglottis	intercostal	larynx	pleura
pulmonary	trachea		

```
T H P R I M R P R P N N T I O A L I R X P A P S T
P R R O R A E T E R H S L E A O E E A I A R L N P
L I T A N P T A A L A L T O L L T P L O O A N P L
I L N P E O I M G E O R P Y E R C O B E N E U O P
R O O T E N G H T N M Y G V T E P R R P R L I A A
O R L O E L O I E E H L R C O V O T N Y M R B P I
R O U T G R T O I C L E L G T N T H R O C A G M R
O A H A R S C H T G A O P X C D N A N T O A I O C
L R T D Y N S O A U O T I H P L O A L L R L I E U
A E I M A M T N S S A S I B L S R A L A O E E T A
C E P S H O L R A T A A O A B Y A A O E R I G L T
L R R I E R L E V P A L S G T T R L V D E U L R N
A A L A G A N O T E L L O T T O H L A R V C E L E
H N R E T L E E E I L R Y N Y C A C R R I N P L D
T O T Y L I O N A I E E O C A A I C A T A L P O P
N G P E N I O T H L M E O I P O N O I H R L L R A
O L I R O X D L T G I H I L X E R E O V G I G S T
R Y A C G Y S R A I C T E M D T E I A S N B T I A
L L A E A N E R A A S A H S A O R T E C Y L R T A
I I A R S E H E M I I I H N P G R A A O A A R H A
Y U O T E P E T A M P L A E Y U G I T L A A R I G
Y A O T A C R A U A R T R N A A P G L H C Y T Y R
B U L I L E R L L I U I X R Y V R L P H B P E I L
M B D B S M L B T E I R N C A A N M E A A L E E A
L B X A N A P I E C R L A I A I O A A D A A L N C
```

Wordsearch – the skin

melanin	vitamin d	corneum	clear
prickle cell	germinativum	epidermis	dermis
sebaceous	follicle	papilla	eccrine
apocrine	sensory nerves	blood supply	lymphatic
mast cells	fibroblasts	leucocytes	collagen

```
N E N M D B S B N A Y O N R G L R Y S C B U I   E I
A E L E T D S L L C C   S S H E B C O O I I   P E A
L N M M L   E E L O O M L T L C C R C A C M L T
E A A U E E U I R V O L L E S L A C E I   E E C P L T
C E C L V L C C D C P D L L D A E L R E S A M I   T
T T E U N I A A   C M P   A E   L C L I   A S Y U C
M P R E P S T N E E O H E S G C N B   I   N N S C P
P L S E O L L A I O S M S P U E   I O T P E D M S
E L M S C B A E N N C C R N L P N E M R S A I S M
E N E S B   M E C I T S S E R C P R L A B A P T I
L U U A C S L R R R M L E S M S F L U K T I M L
T A R U T A L S R S R R C B E I I E Y C C I F C T
L R N I   N A O M B C O E V A A M L L C I I V R L
O O Y T E Y O E A R E E R G S C E A E R M C R C M
S E A R I C M E S S E P D C E E U Y C O P U P P
C C L L O M B C I E N E B L I C S O I B C C M U
C M E O V C C M T   E O E O O N R T U I C S S E B
I I L E O P R Y Y I O A U S A E A E S S I O L L O
E L C P E E C R E N R T I I N H P L M M S C E S M
Y O B R D O O C T E I T C I P I C T R S I C R U L
I C R I C S N L L E S A R M A A P E L L B O E M E
N F P U N E I C C E R C Y S P M D I L O S N P P N
L E E E E Y I U S N O L A E I L B O L P R N   E S
L L S A I O E N E P O K S I A V F E S O R U S I N
O D L L M I L S A I G R O S S F Y C C S L L I G
```

Skin quiz

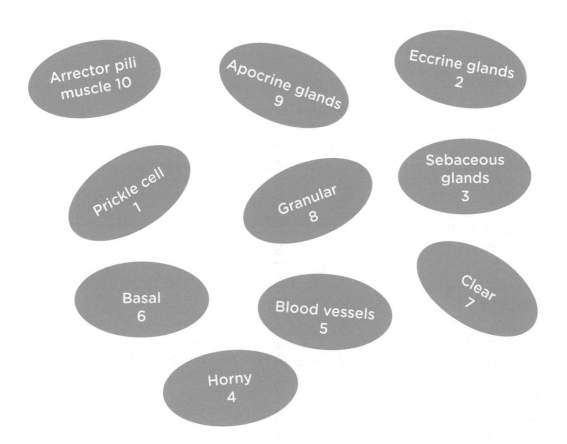

1. Process of keratinisation takes place here ....

2. Dead cells of this layer are rubbed off by friction ....

3. Contracts, causing hair to stand on end ....

4. Layer found on palms of hands and soles of feet... .

5. Send messages to the brain about the sensations of pain, heat and cold ....

6. Deepest layer in epidermis and in contact with the dermis ....

7. Found all over the body and excrete sweat ....

8. Stimulate sweat glands and sebaceous glands to carry out their functions ....

9. Releases a moisturising substance called sebum ....

10. Living cell with a prickly appearance.. .

11. Release milky substance and found in armpit and groin area... .

12. Bring supplies of oxygen and nutrients vital to skin.. .

Answers on page 113.

Mix & Match – the digestive system

Match the words on the left with the correct clues on the right.

1.	Ingestion	1.	Detoxifies the body of drugs and alcohol.
2.	Absorption	2.	This links the pharynx and the stomach.
3.	Proteins	3.	These are emulsified by bile.
4.	Parotid	4.	This is where bile is concentrated and stored.
5.	Digestion	5.	The removal of waste and toxins from the body.
6.	Liver	6.	These are broken down into monosaccharides.
7.	Gall bladder	7.	These are broken down into amino acids.
8.	The oesophagus	8.	Muscular reservoir for food.
9.	Fats	9.	The breakdown of solid foods into constituent parts.
10.	Elimination	10.	The intake of solid food.
11.	Carbohydrates	11.	Salivary glands.
12.	The stomach	12.	The broken down foods taken into the circulation.

Mix & Match – the skeletal system

Match the words on the left with the correct clues on the right.

1.	Kyphosis	1.	Conditions that are hereditary.
2.	Comminuted	2.	A solid structure found on the outside of most bones.
3.	Congenital	3.	Lateral Curvature of the spine.
4.	Impacted	4.	Curvature of the spine outward from the spine.
5.	Scoliosis	5.	Fracture of the bone in several places.
6.	Compact	6.	Supports the bones of the limbs.
7.	Appendicular	7.	A broken bone that has one end driven into the other, like one car shunting into the back of another.

Answers on page 113.

Multiple choice questions

Circle the correct answer. You can check your answers on page 113.

THE CELL

1. The function of lysosomes in a cell is to:
A. help in cell division.
B. produce proteins.
C. produce ATP for energy.
D. produce digestive enzymes.

2. The process of mitosis takes place in phases. Select the correct order:
A. Prophase, anaphase, metaphase, telophase
B. Metaphase, prophase, anaphase, telophase
C. Prophase, metaphase, telophase, anaphase
D. Prophase, metaphase, anaphase, telophase

TISSUES

1. Simple, stratified, cuboidal, ciliated and columnar describe which type of tissue?
A. Areolar
B. Epithelial
C. White fibrous
D. Muscular

2. Transitional tissue is found in:
A. the ovaries.
B. the ear.
C. the bladder.
D. the eyes.

THE SKELETAL SYSTEM

1. What name is given to the cheekbones?
A. Zygomatic
B. Mandible
C. Maxilla
D. Turbinator

2. The sacrum is composed of:
A. four fused bones.
B. six fused bones.
C. five fused bones.
D. three fused bones.

THE MUSCULAR SYSTEM

1. The function of a ligament is to:
A. contract to stabilise joints.
B. strengthen and stabilise joints, connecting bone to bone.
C. connect muscles to bones.
D. stretch to stabilise joints.

2. The middle of a muscle is called the:
A. origin.
B. insertion.
C. belly.
D. attachment.

THE CARDIOVASCULAR SYSTEM

1. The reduction in the blood's ability to carry oxygen is described as:
A. low blood pressure.
B. anaemia.
C. phlebitis.
D. Hodgkin's disease.

2. The superior vena cava carries blood:
A. to the lungs.
B. back to the heart from the lower limbs.
C. back to the heart from the head, neck and arms.
D. from the heart to the tissues of the body.

THE LYMPHATIC SYSTEM

1. The supratrochlear lymph nodes are found:
A. near the elbow.
B. in the head.
C. in the abdomen.
D. in the knee.

2. Blood is filtered by a lymphatic organ as part of our immune system. This is the:
A. heart.
B. spleen.
C. lymph nodes.
D. cisterna chyli.

THE NERVOUS SYSTEM
1. **Neurons receive information through their:**
A. dendrites.
B. nodes of Ranvier.
C. axons.
D. Schwann cells.

2. **The brain controls appetite, thirst and temperature regulation. These centres are found in the:**
A. pituitary gland.
B. cerebrum.
C. thalamus.
D. hypothalamus.

THE ENDOCRINE SYSTEM
1. **Calcium levels in the blood are controlled by which hormones?**
A. Thyroxin and calcitonin
B. Calcitonin and parathormone
C. Calcitonin and triiodothyronin
D. Parathormone and thyroxine

2. **The Islets of Langerhans are found in the:**
A. tonsils.
B. spleen.
C. kidney.
D. pancreas.

THE DIGESTIVE SYSTEM
1. **Pepsin is found in the:**
A. salivary glands.
B. stomach.
C. liver.
D. pancreas.

2. **Which of the following is an organ of the digestive system?**
A. The oesophagus
B. The lungs
C. The ovaries
D. The heart

THE RESPIRATORY SYSTEM
1. **The diaphragm:**
A. contracts to cause inspiration.
B. relaxes to cause inspiration.
C. contracts to cause expiration.
D. relaxes to cause inhalation.

2. **The trachea is located between:**
A. the pharynx and the larynx.
B. the nasal cavity and the larynx.
C. the larynx and the oesophagus.
D. the larynx and the bronchi.

THE URINARY AND REPRODUCTIVE SYSTEM
1. **Reabsorption in the kidney takes place in the:**
A. glomerular capsule.
B. afferent arteriole.
C. loop of Henle.
D. collecting duct.

2. **The corpus luteum is formed during:**
A. the menstrual phase.
B. the secretory phase.
C. the proliferative phase.
D. ovulation.

THE SKIN
1. **Where would you find stratum lucidum?**
A. In the bones
B. In the muscles
C. In the skin
D. In the brain

2. **What is the common name for comedones?**
A. Freckles
B. Whiteheads
C. Liver spots
D. Blackheads